WHEN CARING COUNTS MOST

A GUIDE
FOR JEWISH
CAREGIVERS

*A Comprehensive
Anthology*

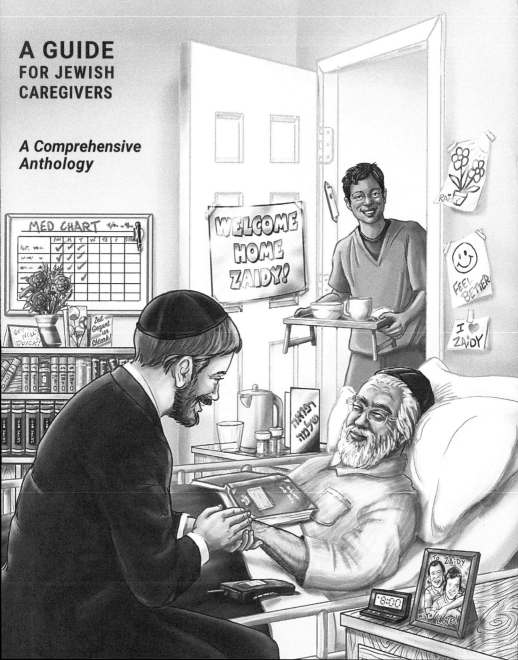

Third Printing April 2021

WHEN CARING COUNTS MOST
© Copyright 2021 by Chevrah Lomdei Mishnah

ISBN: 978-1-944143-20-6

Editor: Mrs. Rivkah Schachnow
Design and Layout: Mrs. Raizy Flamm

Published by
Chevrah Lomdei Mishnah
(732) 364-7029
www.ChevrahLomdeiMishnah.org

Distributed by
The Judaica Press, Inc
123 Ditmas Avenue, Brooklyn, NY 11218
718.972.6200 / 800.972.6201
info@JudaicaPress.com / JudaicaPress.com

THIS BOOK IS DEDICATED
AS A MERIT FOR THE *REFUAH SHELEIMAH* OF

ר' דניאל יצחק בן דבורה
עד מאה ועשרים שנה

A DEAR FRIEND, ACTIVE PARTICIPANT,
AND LONGTIME SUPPORTER OF
CHEVRAH LOMDEI MISHNAH,
WHOSE SAGE ADVICE AND FAR-REACHING VISION
HAVE PLAYED AN INTEGRAL PART IN
CHEVRAH LOMDEI MISHNAH'S
CONTINUED GROWTH AND SUCCESS.

MAY HASHEM GIVE HIM THE HEALTH AND STRENGTH
TO CONTINUE WITH HIS WONDERFUL WORK.

RABBI MOSHE HAIKINS
FOUNDER AND PRESIDENT
CHEVRAH LOMDEI MISHNAH/THE SOCIETY FOR
MISHNAH STUDY

Pesach Tikvah

PESACH TIKVAH/DOOR OF HOPE

FAMILY AND CHILDREN SERVICES

- Family Services
- Outpatient Clinics
- Community Residences
- Geriatric Services

Dear Caregiver,

Caregiving is all about giving. You may be looking after an elderly parent, a spouse, a special-needs child, or a neighbor. Whatever the case may be, it is all about giving. Hashem created a world with endless opportunities to help others, and we need to grab as many as we can.

Whether you came into the caregiving role unwittingly or by intention, whether you received formal training or "learned on the job," you are involved in the highest level of *meleches hakodesh*.

It is our pleasure to present you with this book as a token of appreciation for what you do. You will find within its pages many pearls of wisdom, along with words of *chizzuk*. No professional, whether doctor, nurse, therapist or home attendant, can replace the pure love that you give, albeit under very trying circumstances.

Hashem should reward you for all your efforts. On behalf of the staff of Pesach Tikvah, we wish you every *hatzlachah*!

Dr. Yitschok Shindler
Executive Director

PESACH TIKVAH HOPE DEVELOPMENT, INC.
ADMIN. OFFICES: 365 WILLOUGHBY AVENUE « BROOKLYN, N.Y. 11205 « TEL: (718) 875-6900 « FAX: (718) 875-6999
CONTINUING DAY TREATMENT FAX: (718) 855-4660 « FAMILY SERVICES CENTER FAX: (718) 875-3282

Pesach Tikvah

PESACH TIKVAH/DOOR OF HOPE

FAMILY AND CHILDREN SERVICES

- Family Services
- Outpatient Clinics
- Community Residences
- Geriatric Services

February 2021
Shvat 5781

Dear Reader,

I am grateful for this opportunity to express my appreciation to my devoted and dedicated staff. I know they view their work as more of a calling than a job. Working together as a team, each staff member invests his or her own unique talents to achieve our goals. The fruits of their labors, performed with *achdus*, love and caring for each other and for the many Holocaust survivors and caregivers we help each day, is inspiring.

Zalman Kotzen LCSW
Director of Geriatric Services

PESACH TIKVAH HOPE DEVELOPMENT, INC.
ADMIN. OFFICES: 365 WILLOUGHBY AVENUE « BROOKLYN, N.Y. 11205 « TEL: (718) 875-6900 « FAX: (718) 875-6999
CONTINUING DAY TREATMENT FAX: (718) 855-4660 « FAMILY SERVICES CENTER FAX: (718) 875-3282

Pesach Tikvah

PESACH TIKVAH/DOOR OF HOPE

FAMILY AND CHILDREN SERVICES

- Family Services
- Outpatient Clinics
- Community Residences
- Geriatric Services

Dear Caregiver,

We at Pesach Tikvah began our Holocaust program in 1999, over twenty years ago. Our mission was to provide resources, concrete services and emotional support to survivors, helping them navigate the difficulties associated with aging. As time passed, we watched our survivors slowly shift from independent and vibrant daily living to increased dependence and infirmity. We watched and admired, as you, their children, took on new and difficult responsibilities. With pride and dedication, you accepted your new roles as caregivers to those who cared so deeply for you when you were children and young adults.

Over the years, our mission therefore took on a new dimension, which was to be there for you as we were there for your parents, providing support and *chizuk*, as you do your best under trying circumstances.

With this goal in mind, we created our Enrich program to encourage, advocate, educate and provide respite. We hoped to empower you by connecting you to like-minded caregivers through overnight retreats and dinners. Each event was meticulously planned. Speakers, workshop facilitators, and entertainers were chosen to provide information coupled with recreation so that you would feel cared for and supported.

Unfortunately, Covid has caused a hiccup in our plans and forced us to take a step back. However, we want you to know that we are still here cheering you on from the sidelines. We are always available to answer questions and to continue to lend support.

We hope that you will benefit from the enclosed book, *When Caring Counts Most*, which contains a wealth of information and

Pesach Tikvah | **PESACH TIKVAH/DOOR OF HOPE**
FAMILY AND CHILDREN SERVICES

- Family Services
- Outpatient Clinics
- Community Residences
- Geriatric Services

inspiration. It includes valuable guidance and support from other caregivers; *rabbanim*; and a variety of professionals. Also included is the pamphlet, *Welcome to our Jewish Home: The Home Health Aide's Guide to Basic Jewish Laws and Customs*, which received the *haskamah* of Rabbi Yisroel Belsky, *zt"l*. *When Caring Counts Most* seeks to empower, uplift and encourage you in your challenging role – and by extension, to help your loved one receive the best care possible.

We look forward to seeing you all personally in the very near future.

Wishing you *hatzlachah, simchahs* and nachas from your families.

We wish to acknowledge the guidance, encouragement and financial support of our funding sources: the Jewish Federations of North America, the Claims Conference, and the City Council of New York. Without their help, none of this would be possible.

Sora Blima Gestetner, Bubi Weinberger, Shoshi Soibelman, RuchieWeinberger, Mindy Waldman, and Fraidy Moskovits

Contents

Chapter IV: Protecting Yourself and Your Loved Ones: Advice and Legal Guidance 139

Chapter V: The Value of Life: End-of-Life Challenges 177

≈   ≈   ≈

Introduction

BEING A CAREGIVER FOR A LOVED ONE WHO IS ILL or aging is a very important role, and yet, it is a very daunting one. As a caregiver, one is given the opportunity to help his or her loved one in ways that have never been previously applicable. At the same time, the responsibility is very great, and there is so much to learn. There are medical and legal issues. There are practical implications. And much, much, more.

In conversation, **Rabbi Elchonon Zohn** suggested to me that there was a need for a publication that discusses the varied issues necessary for a caregiver to know. Chevrah Lomdei Mishnah has branched out from an organization that helps people recite Kaddish and finish Mishnah and Gemara *l'zecher nishmas* their loved ones in time for *shloshim* or *yahrtzeit* to publishing numerous books and CDs to assist people grappling with bereavement and loss. Therefore, it is not surprising that Rabbi Zohn recommended that we publish about this topic as well.

The book that you hold in your hands, ***When Caring Counts Most: A Guide for Jewish Caregivers,*** is a compilation of articles that offers information, inspiration, and understanding. It contains advice from rabbis, doctors, lawyers, other professionals, and laypeople offering various perspectives about this overwhelming topic. Some articles have appeared elsewhere and are reprinted here with permission; others were commissioned exclusively for this publication.

Not every article will be applicable to your situation. However, there are many ideas presented here from which you can glean to help you in your role as caregiver. And even though most of the articles are complementary, there are definitely times when authors express contradictory opinions. In such situations, readers are encouraged to seek outside guidance and direction about which approach to take.

Some chapters address the role of care**takers** and aides. These are outside workers who have been hired to assist with the care of the ill or aging individual and should not be confused with the care**giver**, the family member primarily responsible for caring for that person.

We hope that ***When Caring Counts Most: A Guide for Jewish Caregivers*** will empower you with confidence and knowledge, helping you and, in turn, your loved one.

I would like to thank **Rabbi Elchonon Zohn** for giving us the idea to publish this book, as well as for his excitement and involvement in its development and production. He was instrumental in encouraging the writing of articles and obtaining permission for previously published articles to be printed here. That is in addition to his foreword, the article in which he was interviewed, and the article he wrote about *viduy*. Rabbi Zohn is an incredibly busy person and has precious little time available, yet he generously involved himself in this project, ensuring it would be produced in as complete a form as possible.

I would also like to thank all of those who contributed articles, either specifically for this book or by giving permission for their words to be reprinted here. Each article adds another dimension to elucidating what it means to be a caregiver.

Special mention must be made of one contributor in particular, **Mrs. Chaya Leah Rothstein**. Her writing style is engaging, and her articles are very poignant and personal. She submitted numerous vignettes specifically for this book. On top of that, she added an additional feature to this book that hopefully will help many, many people: a pullout pamphlet entitled *Welcome to Our Jewish Home: The Home Health Aide's Guide to Basic Jewish Laws and Customs.* With a *haskamah* from **Rav Yisroel Belsky, zt"l**, this is a handbook for caregivers to give to the aide assisting their loved one, so that he or she can better understand some basic Jewish laws and customs, specifically *kashrus*, Shabbos and Yom Tov, as well as *tzeniyus*. There will be many times in which an uncomfortable situation can easily be avoided if an aide is more familiar with the needs of an Orthodox Jew. We hope this pamphlet will bridge that gap.

A special thank you to **Mrs. Cassandra Lacombe** for her very helpful and useful input regarding *Welcome to our Jewish Home.*

Kudos to our project manager, **Mrs. Miriam Ribiat,** for ensuring that this project was completed in a timely fashion, with all the myriad details involved.

Once again, thank you **Mrs. Rivkah Schachnow** for your careful and insightful editing, and **Mrs. Raizy Flamm,** for your impeccable graphic design.

Thank you to **Mr. Shepsil Scheinberg** for the beautiful cover art.

On a personal note, I would like to thank my wife **Penina and all of our children** for their emotional support. Chevrah Lomdei Mishnah requires much time and effort. Often, it is quite rewarding when we are able to assist *aveilim* or others coping with loss, and when my family sees this on a regular basis, they know, understand, and appreciate what Chevrah Lomdei Mishnah is accomplishing. I gratefully acknowledge their support in this endeavor.

8 Iyyar 5780
Rabbi Moshe Haikins
Founder and President
Chevrah Lomdei Mishnah/The Society for Mishnah Study

Foreword

Rabbi Elchonon Zohn

WHEN LIFE-THREATENING ILLNESS STRIKES, an entire family is plunged into a totally new world. For patients, it is most dramatic: they are facing their own mortality. They likely have unfinished business of various kinds and experience discomfort at the thought of becoming a burden to their loved ones. If they are a parent, they will also have concerns for their family's security – financial and psychological – as well as an overarching anxiety about how the details of a complex medical and emotional situation can possibly be managed.

For the caregiver, whether a spouse, a child, a sibling, or someone else, there are these concerns and so many others as well. Similar concerns arise for those caring for aging relatives. How will they add new responsibilities to their already hectic lives? How will they be able to make medical decisions, especially since *halachic* and ethical issues may arise, and there may not be consensus within the family on a course of action? Practical, ethical, medical, interpersonal, religious, emotional, and financial concerns all come into play. How can a caregiver cope with this new world? He or she will experience moments of fear, of emotional and physical overload, of self-doubt. And all the while, questions with no possible answers will arise: Why is this happening? How long will it go on? The questions are serious, reasonable – and endless.

The uncertainty inherent in such situations is itself extremely stressful. As the Metzudas David on Mishlei 15:30 says, *"Ein b'olam simchah k'hataras hasefeikos"* – "there is no greater possible joy than the joy of eliminating doubt – of certainty." While there will always be uncertainties in situations of serious illness, to the extent that we

---

Rabbi Elchonon Zohn founded the National Association of Chevra Kadisha (NASCK) as a unifying entity for Chevros Kadisha throughout the United States and Canada. He has been the Director of the Chevrah Kadisha of the Va'ad Harabbanim of Queens for over thirty years. Rabbi Zohn received semichah from Yeshivas Chofetz Chaim.

can provide guidance and direction to the caregiver we will have significantly reduced his or her sense of being overwhelmed.

Although I have answered thousands of end-of-life questions over the last thirty-plus years, I was caught completely off-guard when asked to suggest a book that offers guidance and *chizzuk* to caregivers of people with long-term illnesses. I couldn't think of a single book that specifically addressed this topic and this audience! While there are excellent articles and *divrei Torah* on many of these subjects, to my knowledge they had never been collected in one place to serve as a general guide for individuals and families going through such times of crisis.

I immediately thought of **Rabbi Moshe Haikins** and **Chevrah Lomdei Mishnah** as the address to fill this need. They were clearly the ones for the job, since they have created straightforward resource materials for so many end-of-life events. These are situations that most people have little knowledge of, in part because the issues are uncomfortable, and our natural tendency is to shy away from them.

When Caring Counts Most: A Guide for Jewish Caregivers is intended to address, in one place, the many challenges caregivers face at this critical time – a time that can span many years – and to act as a resource to answer the myriad questions that will arise during this journey.

This book does not attempt to replace consultation with a *rav. Daas Torah* is the foundation of Jewish life, and the need for a qualified *rav* is crucial in situations of life and death. It is best if the family has a *rav* who is not only knowledgeable about the medical and halachic issues but also knows the individuals involved. It also is best to involve one's *rav* at the very beginning of the process and not when facing a crisis, when the situation has become "now or never" and the windows of opportunity are rapidly closing. At such times, there is a much greater risk that mistakes will be made because of the pressures of the moment.

The need for guidance may be most pronounced at the onset of an illness, but time will lead caregivers to new questions, new crises, new sources of stress: what end-of-life conversations, if any, to have with the dying person, be they a parent, spouse, or other relative? When is it best to hold these conversations? How and when do you say goodbye? When should a person in a life-threatening situation say *viduy*? Should family be notified or encouraged to come at a particular time when the end is possibly near?

When Caring Counts Most is intended to complement the *da'as Torah* the family receives. This book anticipates and explicates the common issues that arise throughout the progression of terminal illness.

We know that the word *nisayon*, "challenge" or "test," comes from the same root as *neis*, which can mean both "miracle" and "flag." What unites these seemingly unrelated words is the concept of being "raised." A miracle raises one's faith to a new level, and a raised flag is a symbol that allows people to rally around it, to express their allegiance to and pride in their country or their cause. So, too, a challenge or test, when properly met and overcome, will raise and increase one's strength of character and one's ability to serve Hashem.

When Caring Counts Most comes to fill a void: to provide direction and *chizzuk* to people throughout the most trying and stressful period of their lives; to make this most difficult experience as comfortable as possible, as meaningful as possible, and as successful – yes, successful – as possible; to help the family turn its *nisayon* into an opportunity to raise themselves, and those around them, emotionally and spiritually, individually and collectively.

The greatest gift those facing a challenge can receive is clear direction and practical advice. With these in hand, they can meet the challenge with the comfort and even the *simchah* – the inner peace – that only clarity can provide.

We offer a resounding *yasher ko'ach* to **Chevrah Lomdei Mishnah** and wish them the greatest *hatzlachah* in bringing this important work to the Jewish community.

CHAPTER I

A Torah Perspective on Caregiving

Today is a Gift

Rabbi Paysach Krohn

[The following article has been adapted from a lecture given by Rabbi Krohn for Sparks of Life, an organization that supports those with Parkinson's Disease and their families. Rabbi Krohn's message is equally applicable to anyone caring for a loved one who is ill or infirm. Transcription and adaptation of the lecture for this publication were with Rabbi Krohn's permission. -Ed.]

Every Day Counts

IN DOING RESEARCH TO PUT TOGETHER THIS PIECE, I realized that there are three different groups affected by illness: the individual who is not well, the caregiver, and the family. As a matter of fact, one of the books I read mentions that the caregiver is really a hidden patient, and the caregiver really has to be addressed and guided not to lose themselves because they are so totally devoted to the patient.

The more I read, the more I was reminded about a certain poem I once heard many years ago from a geriatrician. He told me that he had an elderly patient who was not well and very, very forgetful, but there was one thing that she remembered. Every single time this doctor walked into her room, she always recited this poem:

> *Yesterday is history.*
> *Tomorrow is a mystery.*
> *Today is a gift of G-d.*
> *That's why we call it the present.*

That's when I thought about the family of the ill person. Yesterday is history. Once a person is diagnosed with a terminal illness, it's never going to go back to the way it was. Yesterday is history. Those days are over. Unfortunately, there is not yet a cure.

Rabbi Paysach J. Krohn is an Orthodox rabbi, mohel, author, and lecturer on topics related to ethics and spiritual growth. He is the author of the bestselling "Maggid" series of books for ArtScroll, inspired by the stories of Rabbi Sholom Schwadron, who was known as the "Maggid of Yerushalayim."

Tomorrow is a mystery because very often, no one can predict the progressiveness or the advancement of the ailment, and so tomorrow is a mystery.

But today is a gift of Hashem. That's why we call it the present.

That's what I think the guidepost has to be for the individual who is suffering, for the caregiver, and for the family. Let's live one day at a time. Forget about what happened yesterday. We don't know what will be tomorrow. Let's live one day at a time.

Let me share an amazing story, which I always tell when I visit the *kever* of the Sefas Emes in Warsaw. The Sefas Emes was unfortunately *niftar* at the relatively young age of 58. At his *levayah*, his son, who would eventually become the next Gerrer Rebbe, the Imrei Emes, said to one of his brothers, "At least our father had *arichas yamim*." The brother replied, "Our father only lived 58 years. That's not *arichas yamim*." The Imrei Emes responded with a brilliant answer: "I didn't say he had *arichas* **shanim**, length of **years**. I said he had *arichas* **yamim**, length of **days**."

There's a big difference between *arichas shanim* and *arichas yamim*. No one, no *rav*, no doctor, no one can guarantee *arichas shanim* for themselves. Nobody knows what will happen tomorrow. Nobody can guarantee that they will live a long life as far as years, but every single one of us can guarantee that we have *arichas yamim*. That's what the Imrei Emes meant. The Sefas Emes had length of days. Every day of his life counted. Every day was special. Every day he accomplished something. That's why he had *arichas yamim*. His days just didn't fly by without accomplishment.

One of the people I became very close to over the years was Rebbetzin Esther Jungreis. She was a very sensitive person who had a very good marriage. Her husband, unfortunately, passed away young, and she told me, and eventually wrote this in a book called *Life is a Test,* that when he passed away, she could not pick up his papers and his notes. It was so painful for her to see his writings that she couldn't even pick them up – until one day when one of her daughters showed her a note that her husband had written, and she felt that this was a message her husband was giving to her. Once she read this note she was able to read everything else that he had written.

You know what he wrote? "A long life is not good enough, but a good life is long enough." That's a great expression for everyone to know. Just because somebody has *arichas shanim* and lives until 90, it doesn't mean he lived a good life. He lived a long life. But a good life is long enough. And every person, no matter what ailment they have, can live a good life. Every person who makes every day count can live a good life.

After sharing this idea in her book, Rebbetzin Jungreis added the following thought:

> *The goodness cannot be measured by the length of our years, but by how we live those years. The goodness is not about what we amass, but what we give. It's not about having more, but being more. For in the end, our lives are judged not by the businesses and the houses and the portfolios we built, but by the lives we touched and we made better.*

And as a caregiver, it's important to realize that you are living a life of giving, and you are making every day valuable.

I'll tell you something amazing. There's a very interesting question that all of us have thought about at one time or another. Why don't we recite *shehecheyanu* when we start counting *sefirah*? On every other mitzvah that we perform once a year, whether it's shofar, *megillah*, or *matzah*, we say *shehecheyanu*. So why don't we say *shehecheyanu* when we start counting *sefirah*?

The Bnei Yissaschar answers this question: "*Ki ein hateshukah al hayamim hanisparim*," the main thing is not the counting of the days, but rather, that every day you continue to move higher and higher and higher, and then at the end of the 49 days, when you reach that pinnacle of Shavuos, you recite *shehecheyanu*. The days of *sefirah* are not only about counting days. *Sefirah* is about making your days count.

During these days, we want to make every day count so that we can look back at each day and say, "You know something? On this day, I accomplished this." And then, as those accomplishments accrue and we reach that exalted level on Shavuos, we recite *shehecheyanu* because that's what *shehecheyanu* is all about. It's not only the *berachah* of *shehecheyanu* to which this applies; this is a guide for life. We have lived a good life when we accomplished and made every day special.

I WANT TO SHARE WITH YOU SOMETHING THAT PERHAPS you never thought about. Every person in life, every caregiver, every

Never Give Up Hope family member, all of us, should remember this unbelievable lesson about Rabi Akiva.

We all know that the Gemara in *Yevamos* (*62b*) tells us that Rabi Akiva lost 24,000 *talmidim*, The *lashon* in the *medrash* is that they all died during that 33-day period, *vekulan b'perek echad meisu* (*Bereishis Rabbah 61:3*).

Have you ever done the math? 24,000 *talmidim* died in a period of 33 days. That's 727 *talmidim* dying every day! Imagine you are Rabi Akiva, and every day you get the *besurah*. The *talmid* from Haifa, Rebbi, the one you loved so much. You've got to go up to be *menachem aveil*. Rebbi, you've got to give a *hesped* in Tel Aviv. That was the *iluy*. That was the kid who just got married. Rebbi, this *ben yachid*. Rebbi, that *baki b'Shas*. And he's running from Ashdod, and he's running to Ashkelon. What would we do? We would go crazy. If you were a *rebbi* and had 727 *talmidim* dying a day, you would go crazy, and you would say, "Okay, Hashem, I get it. *I'm out of here.* I'm not going to teach Torah anymore because obviously You don't like my *talmidim*; You don't like me; You don't like what I taught." That's what any normal person would say if Hashem punished him in such a way.

What did Rabi Akiva do? You know what he did? It's unbelievable. He took five *talmidei chachamim*, the *medrash* tells us, and he said to them, "*Rabbosai*, listen. We made a mistake. We didn't teach them to give *kavod* to one another. Let's start all over again. We're not giving up."

And those five *talmidim*, the *medrash* tells us, eventually taught Torah throughout the whole Eretz Yisrael!

Isn't that incredible? You know what we learn from Rabi Akiva? We learn not to give up! You think your loved one has a difficult illness or condition and the world is over? Just the opposite. You didn't lose 727 *talmidim* a day. And what did Rabi Akiva do? He was not afraid. Instead he said, "Hashem, this is my challenge. I'm up to it. If You gave it to me, I can handle this. I'm going to start all over again because I know what I'm doing is right, and You know what I'm doing is right. So I made a mistake, I didn't teach them about *middos*, I'll fix it." And that's what he did.

You know who Rabi Akiva was? Many of us are familiar with the final page in *Makkos*. Rabi Akiva was walking with a group of *talmidei chachamim* and they saw a fox at the place where the Beis Hamikdash had been. They began to cry, "This is where the Beis Hamikdash once stood and a fox is roaming here?" Rabi Akiva, on the other hand, began to laugh. They said, "Rebbi what are you laughing about?"

He replied, "What are you crying about?"

"Cry? We shouldn't cry? This is the place of the *churban Beis Hamikdash*, and a fox is walking where the *Kohen Gadol* used to walk!"

Rabi Akiva said, "What are you saying? That's the best news in the world. You know why? Because the *navi* predicted that this was going to happen, and the *navi* also predicted (*Zechariah 8:4*) that *od yeshvu zekeinim u'zekeinos birechovos Yerushalayim*, there will yet be old men in Yerushalayim, and they're going to be walking with their canes and they're going to live long days, and the boys and the girls are going to play in the streets. Everyone is going to be so happy. So if the first part of the *nevu'ah* came true, then the second part will come true as well. The fact that the *navi's* words are coming to fruition is something to smile about."

Rabi Akiva was positive. Rabi Akiva was not afraid of the situation. Rabi Akiva saw the challenge, he accepted it, and he built on it. And that's what every one of us has to do. In life, a Jew can get discouraged but he should never feel broken. If Rabi Akiva was broken, he wouldn't have started all over again with five more *talmidim*. Of course he was discouraged. Anybody can be discouraged, but a Jew can never, *chas v'Shalom*, become broken. A Jew never gives up.

I KNOW THAT MANY PEOPLE DEEP DOWN WANT TO ASK, "Why me? Hashem, why did You do this to me? I'm such a good person. I've done so much good in my life. I raised my kids to be *ehrlich*. I always *davened*. I always did *mitzvos*. Why was I chosen to suffer this way?"

We Never See the Whole Picture

Are we allowed to ask such a question?

The Gemara in *Bava Basra* tells us that the answer, amazingly, is yes! The Gemara (*Bava Basra 17*) says: "*Amar Iyov*, Iyov said to the Hashem. Ribbono Shel Olam, you give me so many *tzaros, shema ru'ach se'arah avrah lefanecha,* maybe a whirlwind got into Your mind.

V'nischalef bein oyev l'Iyov, and you got confused: *oyev* is an enemy, Iyov is my name. Maybe You got it mixed up. I'm not Your enemy. What are You doing?"

If we wouldn't see this in the Gemara, we wouldn't be able to say this! But the Gemara is telling us that this is what Iyov said, and Hashem didn't become angry with him. Hashem gave him the following answer (*Iyov 38:4*): "*Eifoh hayisah b'yasdi aretz,* where were you when I formed this world? *Hagged,* you tell Me, *im yadata binah,* if you're so smart."

In other words, "I have a Master Plan. You live for 70, 80, 90 years. You think you understand everything. You weren't around when I started the world."

Rabbi Zev Leff cites a beautiful *mashal* from the Chafetz Chayim. How many times have we said the *passuk* in *Ashrei:* "*Shomer Hashem es kol ohavav,* Hashem protects all those that He loves, *ve'eis kol haresha'im yashmid,* and all the *resha'im* He annihilates."

Imagine that a fellow comes late to *shul* and hears the following: *Es kol ohavav ve'eis kol haresha'im yashmid,* all those that He loves and all the *resha'im* He annihilates. He thinks, *Hey, Hashem, what are You doing?* But remember, he walked in late! If you walk in late, you haven't heard the whole *passuk.* You can't come in the middle of a *shiur* and ask a *kasha.* You can't be watching a video and say, "Why did this happen?" You weren't there at the beginning!

And if the fellow leaves early, what does he hear? *Shomer Hashem es kol ohavav, ve'eis kol haresha'im,* Hashem protects all whom He loves and all the *resha'im.* Again, he wants an explanation for Hashem's actions. But if he didn't stick around for the end of the show, he can't ask questions!

We don't live long enough, so we can't start asking *kashas.* Hashem has been around forever; Mashiach will hopefully arrive tomorrow, but if not, the latest he'll be here is the year 6000, so there's a long story here. You're asking questions? You walk in in the middle, you come in late, you're leaving early, how can you ask anything? This is what Hashem told Iyov – but He didn't get angry. He didn't say you're not allowed to ask that question. Everybody is allowed to ask that question, and everybody is allowed to be given the answer that we don't live long enough to understand Hashem's Master Plan.

RAV MORDECHAI SCHWAB, WHO WAS THE *MASHGIACH* IN Yeshiva Bais Shraga in Monsey, had a *talmid*, Rabbi Zev Smith, who is a brilliant *talmid chacham*. Rabbi Smith told me that he used to go visit his *rebbi* every *chol hamo'ed*. One year, before his visit on *Chol Hamo'ed Sukkos*, a member of the Schwab family called him to say, "I want you to know that your *rebbi* is very sick. You're not going to recognize him. He's very pale and frail. If you want to come, you can come with your family, and we'll welcome you, but just remember that he doesn't look the way he looked six months ago on *Chol Hamo'ed Pesach*."

Rabbi Smith decided to go anyway. He shared that as much as the family had prepared him, when he walked into that room, he almost fainted. His beloved *rebbi* looked so pale and so frail and so thin. But Rav Mordechai Schwab was brilliant. He took one look at Rabbi Smith and said, "*Daiga nit*, don't worry, *ich leb b'simchah*, I'm living with happiness." He told Rabbi Smith that he hadn't been able to go to *shul* on Yom Kippur. "You don't think I want to *daven*? I wanted to *daven*. I didn't make myself sick. Hashem made me sick. He said I can't learn anymore because I get headaches when I learn. You don't think I want to learn? I want to learn, but Hashem gave me the headaches. I didn't give myself the headaches." And then he shared a very powerful message, "*Ich leb chayim biretzono*."

We say this every morning in *davening*, *ki rega be'apo chayim biretzono*, but Rav Schwab translated it as follows: *chayim*, I am living, *biretzono*, the way He wants me to live. If He wants me to live but I can't *daven*, I'm okay with that. If He wants me to live but I can't learn, that's His business. That's what He wants? I'm okay with it. And nobody should feel bad if their loved one is ill, and they can't do a mitzvah or they can't learn. This is what Hashem wants from them right now, and if that's what He wants, *chayim biretzono*, he or she is living the way Hashem wants. There's no reason to get down about it. Hashem orchestrated it that he or she can't do *mitzvos*, We have to serve Him in the way that we can, as well as we can, but we certainly shouldn't feel bad or look down on somebody who can't do *mitzvos* in such a situation.

I remember speaking to Rav Gifter, *zecher tzaddik livrachah*, when he had Parkinson's Disease. I used to visit him in Camp Agudah. Without a doubt in my mind he would have been the *Gadol Hador*. If he hadn't had Parkinson's, he would have been the one everybody would have listened to after Rav Moshe Feinstein and Rav Ya'akov Kamenetsky and Rav Aharon Kotler were *niftar*. But Hashem gave him Parkinson's, so he couldn't do it.

Was Rav Nosson Tzvi Finkel any less because he had Parkinson's? Every single time I went to Rav Nosson Tzvi and I would talk to him, I would just start crying. I was so taken by the *heilegkeit* of that Yid. I remember I had the *zechus* to be a *mohel* once or twice when he was *sandek*. Somebody had to hold his hands because he was shaking the whole time, but would anybody dare not to use him as a *sandek*? What a *kavod*. A *heilege* Yid. That's what Hashem wanted, so he was okay with that.

We don't look down at these people if they're minimized in what they can accomplish. *Chayim biretzono*, that's the attitude for us to have about our loved ones, and that's the attitude we can encourage them to have: Don't feel bad; feel great. You're doing the best that you can do, and you're the biggest *tzaddik* and *tzaddeikes* around because you're doing what Hashem wants under these conditions. You didn't give it to yourself; He did.

If that's the case, what can we do to make life pleasant for those that are limited by illness? There was a study that was done recently about how happy people can be even in illness, and it showed that those people that had a happy demeanor in their illness got along better, they healed quicker, and they accomplished more. Two people can have the exact same illness, but if you could somehow get somebody to feel good about themselves and feel happy about their position, they will heal better. They'll do better. And the same is true for caregivers, who are often dealing with a great deal of stress.

Mishenichnas Adar marbin b'simchah, when Adar comes we increase our *simchah*. Rav Pam once shared a beautiful expression with me: people are always looking for the city of happiness, but they don't realize that it's in the state of mind.

You know what occurred to me after I heard that? Write down the word *machshavah*. It's amazing! It has the same *osiyos* as *b'simchah*! *Mishenichnas Adar marbin b'simchah* = *machshavah*. Happiness is in the mind. Two people can have the same situation. One can be so thrilled, *chayim biretzono*, I'm okay. *Ich leb b'simchah*. It's amazing that Rav Schwab said *b'simchah*. That's *machshavah*. No matter what the situation, the Eibershter put you there – that's the key. Are we allowed to ask why? Of course. But we don't know the answer, so we go on. We get discouraged, but we don't become broken.

THERE WAS A STUDY THAT SHARED EIGHT THINGS A person can do that will bring them happiness. I'll share two:

How to Live with Happiness

One is to start a daily gratitude journal. What are you grateful for today? Write it down. At the end of the week, you'll have seven things you're grateful for. Most of us are grateful for our spouses. Most of us are grateful for our kids. All of us are grateful for our grandchildren, and great-grandchildren. Write it down. Once a day. And then look at it. And encourage the person you are caring for to do so as well, if he or she is able.

A lady called me recently and said, "Rabbi Krohn, I need *chizzuk*." She told me that her husband wasn't well, they needed *parnassah, shidduchim*. My first reaction was, *what am I, instant coffee? I don't even know you*. But then I told her, "I want to give you some homework." I asked her, "Do you own your house?" She answered in the affirmative. "Do you have grandchildren?" Again, she answered that she did. I told her to write down all the wonderful things with which she had been blessed and to keep it on an index card and before saying *modim* in *Shemoneh Esreih,* to read those things. It was good homework. I spoke to her a few weeks later. I can't say that she was cured, but it certainly made an impression. Keep a gratitude journal.

Here's the second thing, and I'm a big believer in this. Do a *chessed* a day for another person. Not a husband for a wife or a wife for a husband. That you've got to do if you know what's good for you. I'm talking about doing a *chessed* for someone out of the house. I'm going to tell you something I did, of which I'm very proud. When my Tante Liba was ill, I wrote her a postcard every single day. I would go to an airport and buy ten postcards, and I sent her a postcard every day. After she passed away, she had 500 or 600, at least! Imagine that. A lady is stuck at home. She's such a lovely lady, but she can't get out for whatever reason, and somebody remembers her with a little postcard. I didn't write any big *chiddushim*, but it's a *chessed* to make someone feel remembered and special. Every day from tonight on, do something special for somebody else and write it down. I am telling you that your life will change, and you know how I know that your life will change? Because as David HaMelech writes in Tehillim, *Hashem tzilcha* – Hashem is your shadow. You do for others; others will do for you.

The Chafetz Chayim writes (*Ahavas Chessed, chelek 2, perek 4*): "*U'me'od tzarich lizaher shelo yachsor lo middas hachessed afilu lo yom echad*" – not one day should go by in your life that you don't do a favor for somebody else. Similarly, a Jew is supposed to learn every day, and this applies to women as well. A woman might learn *Chumash* or *Tanach* or *mussar*. She could read a Maggid book or learn *Shulchan Aruch* or learn something in *tefillah*. Every day you've got to learn something. And every day you've got to do a favor for somebody.

And then the Chafetz Chayim writes something that is really frightening! "*K'she'asak b'Torah bilvad*, if somebody is just learning and he doesn't do *chessed*, *v'gemillus chassadim lo asah kera'oi lo*, and he doesn't do *chessed* the way he's supposed to, *lo nis'arer al yado l'ma'aleh middas hachessed, chas v'Shalom*, then Hashem is not going to do *chessed* with him." We all need Hashem's *chessed* every day; every time we go on a highway; every time we open a business; every time we make a business deal. You want Hashem's *chessed*? You've got to do *chessed*.

The Chafetz Chayim says that Torah is not enough. Torah is a *gevaldige zechus*, and with it, you'll have a straight ticket to the *Olam HaEmes*, but we want *chessed* in this world. We want our children to be protected. We want to be protected ourselves.

Therefore, the Chafetz Chayim says you've got to do a *chessed* every day. He says that if a person is worthy of some kind of suffering or judgment – and we all know we're guilty of certain things – Hashem is not going to help him unless he did *chessed*. But if you keep a *chessed* notebook, or encourage somebody who is homebound to do so, and then at the end of a week you say, "Look at that. I lived for somebody else. I did a *chessed* for somebody. I called somebody in the nursing home. I did a favor for somebody. I was shopping and then I called a single mother from the store to say, 'Hey listen, I'm here anyway. What could I get for you?' " then you've done something that day. Then you have *arichas yamim*. Then no matter how much effort and time you're expending caring for a loved one or what illness they may have, you're doing something special, and that's what *shehecheyanu* is all about.

In *Sanhedrin* (98), Rabi Elazar was asked, "*Mah ya'aseh adam,* what should a person do, *v'yinatzel meichevlei Mashiach,* that you should be saved from the pains of Mashiach? The Gemara answers: *Ya'asok b'Torah u'gemillus chassadim* – do Torah and *chessed* every day. From now on, let every person make up that not a day should go by without learning Torah and doing *chessed.* Then you'll feel great about yourself. And the truth is, caring for a sick relative is a great *chessed.* So no matter how difficult it is to take care of your loved one, you're doing what Hashem wants. That's the greatest feeling in the world.

I JUST WANT TO END WITH THESE THOUGHTS. THERE'S something that I find gives me *chizzuk* every morning when I *daven*
Anything Can Happen these words, and every person with an ill family member should think about this. In the *Birkas Kri'as Shema* we say that Hashem is *zore'a tzeddakos, matzmi'ach yeshu'os* – Hashem makes salvations flourish and then, *borei refuos.* Hashem is the One Who creates healing, Who creates new cures. So just because in the books they say that there's no cure for a disease, it doesn't mean that tomorrow it can't happen. And right afterward the *berachah* continues: *hamechadesh b'tuvo b'chol yom tamid* – Hashem is a *mechadesh.* Tomorrow a cure could emerge. Some doctor in Chile could come up with something, and everybody with a previously incurable disease will be cured. Anything could happen.

Have you ever noticed that *refa'einu* is the eighth *berachah* in *Shemoneh Esreih*?

The Gemara tells us in Megillah (*17b*): "*Mah ra'u lomar refuah b'shemonah* – why is *refuah* the eighth *berachah*? *Mitoch shenitnah milah b'shminis,* because a *mohel* does a *bris* on the baby on the eighth day, and the baby needs *refuah.* That's why *refa'einu* is the eighth *berachah.*

I want to add something more. The Maharal writes that the number eight is *l'ma'alah miderech hateva.* Seven is complete. Eight is *l'ma'alah miderech hateva.* You know why *refuah* is number eight? Because *refuah* can happen at any time, *l'ma'alah miderech hateva.* There's no cure for cancer? So far, there's no cure. There's no cure for Alzheimer's? So far. *Refuah* is eight. Anything could happen. A Jew should never, ever give up.

I WANT TO END WITH A MAGNIFICENT STORY. THERE WAS a man named Rav Yeshayah Bardaki. Rav Yeshayah Bardaki was a

Giving Hashem the Strength to Save You

talmid of Rav Chaim Volozhiner. He lived in a country in which the Jews were persecuted, and he was desperate to escape with his children. Every night there was a fisherman who would smuggle people to a country on the other side of the river. But the boat was getting ricketier every night because instead of holding 20 or 30 people, the fisherman would cram it with 70 people.

On the night that Rav Yeshayah Bardaki and his two sons were on the boat, it split apart; there were not enough rafts, and people panicked. They were less than a quarter of a mile away from shore, and suddenly Rav Yeshayah realized he was in the water holding two kids, a ten-year-old boy and a six-year-old boy. He knew he couldn't swim holding both boys. Suddenly, he was faced with the most difficult decision possible. He was going to have to let one of the children go. He was sobbing as he told his children, "Boys, there's no point in the three of us dying. I can only carry one of you. I don't know what to do. Tell me what should I do."

The older boy said, "Tatty, drop me. My younger brother doesn't know how to swim. I know how to swim a little bit. Maybe I'll make it. Let me go."

The younger boy said, "No Tatty, drop me because my brother is a *tzaddik*. He learns Torah. He learns Gemara already. He has more *zechusim* than me. Let me go and hold onto him."

The father didn't know what to do. He felt his strength ebbing, and he knew he was going to drown. He decided to drop the older boy, and as he let go of the boy, although previously he had told his father to hold onto his younger brother instead of him, the boy began to beg, "Tatty, please don't drop me. Don't drop me." The father couldn't do it. He just couldn't leave go of his child. So he hung onto both of them, and then, somehow, miraculously, he was able to reach the shore. Once there, he fell onto the sand and collapsed. When he finally had the strength to get up, the older boy said, "Tatty, how can I thank you? You saved my life."

Rav Yeshayah responded, "I didn't save your life. You saved your life. I didn't have the strength to carry you, but when you cried out to me in such a way, you gave me a strength that I didn't even know I had. Without your cries, I never would have had that strength. Your cries gave me that strength. That's why I was able to save you."

In *Berachos* (*32*), it says that *leiv* is heart. *Tefillah* is *avodah shebaleiv*. The Gemara tells us, "*Im ro'eh adam she'hispallel,*" that if a person sees that he *davened, velo ne'eneh,* and he wasn't answered, he shouldn't give up. *Yachzor v'yispallel,* he should *daven* again. You know why? Because the *passuk* says, "*Kaveh el Hashem, chazzak v'ya'ameitz libecha v'kavei el Hashem,*" hope to Hashem, *chazzak v'ya'ameitz libecha,* make your heart strong, and then it says again, *vekavei el Hashem.*

Why does the *passuk* say it that second time? Because sometimes we don't have enough *zechusim,* and so to speak, Hashem doesn't have enough strength to save us because we don't deserve it. So what do we do? We cry out like that little boy cried, and when the little boy cried, he gave strength to his father that his father didn't even know he had. That's what Hashem says. That's what the Gemara is telling us. Sometimes you don't have enough *zechusim.* You've got to *daven* again. Give Hashem that strength, that *ko'ach,* to save you because now when you *daven* you have earned more *sechar.*

Never, ever give up. Ever! We can all live productive lives, *chayim biretzono.* Do a *chessed.* Learn something. You'll have *arichas yamim.* You could be discouraged, but don't be broken. If we have that spark within us to do *chessed,* to do Torah, we'll have life. We'll have the real life. Our loved one may not have *arichas* **shanim**, but we can all have *arichas* **yamim**.

Hashem should *bentch* each and every one of us. We should be able to give *chizzuk* to each other. We should be able to give strength to those who need it and never forget to give strength to ourselves and to know that any position in which Hashem put us might be challenging, but we are Rabi Akiva's people. We never, ever give up.

KEY POINTS:

- There are three different groups affected by illness: the patient, the caregiver, and the family. In many ways, the caregiver is really a hidden patient. Whichever group you fit into, try to live one day at a time.

- *Arichas yamim* doesn't mean length of years – it means length of days. A person who makes every day count can have a good life, no matter his situation. As a caregiver, you are making every day count.

- We learn from Rabi Akiva – who lost 24,000 *talmidim*, who laughed about the *Churban* when the other Tana'im cried – to remain positive despite the challenges.

- We can question why we are faced with challenges, but we need to accept that we can't understand Hashem's Master Plan.

- We are all living *chayim biretzono* – the way Hashem wants. We should serve Him the way we can, but shouldn't feel bad or look down upon someone who can't do *mitzvos* in their situation.

- People who have a happy demeanor in their illness manage better, heal quicker and accomplish more. The same is true for caregivers, who are often dealing with a lot of stress.

- Two things a person can do to bring themselves happiness: start a happiness journal and do a *chessed* for someone outside your household. Encouraging someone who is homebound to do this as well will give them joy and purpose in life.

- Make up that not a day will go by without learning Torah in some form.

- No matter how difficult it is to care for your loved one, you're doing what Hashem wants. And that's the greatest feeling in the world!

- Just as Hashem is *matzmi'ach yeshu'os* – makes salvations flourish – he is *borei refuos* – creates new cures. Just because there's no cure for a disease today, it doesn't mean it can't happen tomorrow.

- Your *tefillos* can give Hashem the *ko'ach* to save you or your loved one. *Davening* can bring you the extra *zechusim* necessary to deserve the salvation you weren't previously worthy of.

Caregiving: Two as One

Rabbi Yonah Weinrib

WHEN ONE IS BLESSED WITH HEALTH, IT IS A tremendous *berachah*, never to be taken for granted. There are no guarantees for long life, good health, and the myriad acts of kindness that Hashem bestows upon us daily. *"Al nisecha she'b'chol yom imanu"* – this refers to the daily miracles that are with us. The word *imanu*, with us, can also be a reference to HaKaddosh Baruch Hu because unless we recognize that He is always with us, we may overlook all the miracles that He performs.

I WRITE THIS ARTICLE NOT AS A THEORETICAL TREATISE or philosophical discussion of the challenges, but rather the minor triumphs and lessons to be learned from being the caregiver of a loved one. Nearly seven years ago, my

Viewing the Patient's Needs as Your Own

beloved wife Miriam, *a"h*, was brought to her final *menuchah* after living through a debilitating illness – for ten-and-a-half years. It is perhaps the most painful feeling in the world to be the one who is closest to the loved one with an illness and often feel the pain of knowing that we cannot bring about the necessary *refuah*.

Though my experience was with a spouse, there are lessons that can be applied and hopefully sensitivities refined in dealing with an ill parent, sibling or child or anyone in need of a *refuah*. Rav Shimon

Rabbi Yonah Weinrib is an artist/calligrapher who specializes in elaborate, researched-based manuscript illumination. An accomplished author as well as artist, he has published volumes on bar/bas mitzvah; the Jewish wedding; Hallel; the Manuscript Shiron series, the Megillah and an internationally acclaimed edition of Pirkei Avos. He has exhibited and lectured internationally and has been commissioned to design presentation awards for various organizations, as well as heads of state. One of his commissions was for a presentation award by JNF to the King of Jordan. You can visit his site at www.judaicailluminations.com.

Shkop, *zt"l*, in his introduction to his classic work *Sha'arei Yosher,* poses a seeming contradiction in *Pirkei Avos,* chapter 1, Mishnah 14. The Mishnah begins, *"Im ein ani li, mi li* – if I am not to myself, who will be there for me?" Yet the next phrase seems to negate the message of the first: "If I am only for myself, then who am I?" The first statement seems to focus solely on oneself. *"I* am the purpose of my existence – to the exclusion of all others." The second statement seems to say that others are also important, not just myself! Rav Shimon offers a profound insight, which impacts how we look at ourselves, particularly when dealing with others. When a child is born, the entire world revolves around him. He is totally dependent on others to cater to his every need, providing food, seeing to personal hygiene and addressing every discomfort. As he begins to grow, he sees that "I" am not the center of the universe; there are other siblings and individuals who need and deserve attention. He still focuses on "I" – but his definition of "self" is now more inclusive – his own needs have to take into account siblings and family members.

As he grows and begins to establish relationships with others, he finds that there are even more individuals whose needs vie with his own. He is not negating his own needs; his ever-expanding definition of self now includes friends as well. When he grows and matures and seeks to find a spouse, his definition of "I" has to become even greater. The all-inclusive "I" has to address the needs of one who is certainly almost an extension of himself... and so it is throughout his life. The ever-expanding sense of "*ani*" allows him to see the needs of his partner in life as his own. Her needs are her spouse's needs – "*v'hayu l'vasar echad*" takes on a profound and poignant meaning when the care is being given to a spouse or a very close family member.

Creating an Environment: Giving, Taking and Being

ILLNESS BRINGS A FAMILY INTO THE EXPERIENCE OF "THE new-normal"; what was taken for granted days ago as the way the family operated is altered, adjusted or sometimes altogether discarded. The needs of the person who is ill are paramount, surely dependent on the nature of the illness and care plan. Children's schoolwork, mealtimes and life's day-to-day activities take on a new rhythm, factoring in the needs of the one for whom the care is given. Illness can be a great equalizer, so that a person who may have commanded the respect of the community or friends through his work, *chessed* and/or past accomplishments may now be a beneficiary of the *chessed* of others. For so many years the person or family may have been in a position of helping others with their time and resources, and now others are needed to perform basic tasks to assist the individual or family.

So much of being ill, or functioning as the primary caregiver, is centered on one's *emunah* in HaKaddosh Baruch Hu. Having *emunah* in and giving one's life – often literally – over to Hashem is a skill that must be nurtured in the years *before* the onset of an illness. It's virtually impossible for one to "become a *ma'amin*" when the need arises. It is a lifelong process that must start at the beginning of one's years and surely when one enters married life. In our particular situation, I had a "*rebbi* in *emunah*" – my father, *z"l*, a Holocaust survivor who lived through the horrors of Auschwitz with the creed, "*morgen vet zein besser* – tomorrow will be better," to guide him. There were no speeches or lessons on how to live through adversity – he taught by his quiet example. Our family saw him as a living example of perseverance, of clinging to Hashem and living with *emunah peshutah*! This can't be defined as "simple faith" – it was anything but simple; it was awesome. Perhaps it can be defined as "uncomplicated faith," unaffected by life circumstances and the challenges they bring, with a steadfast clinging to Hashem in every situation in life.

When a spouse or parent is ill, it often means humbling oneself to be the recipient of kindness or *chessed*, even when one may have spent years giving to others. The shift that takes place reflects the realities of caregiving, making sure the needs of the one who is ill are met, and rearranging, not negating, one's daily activities. A family that had been relatively self-sufficient in so many areas of life suddenly finds that it relies on a team – of friends, family and community members to juggle life's normal routine. Recognizing that the *rofei chol basar* is in charge of *all* aspects of the *choleh's* care enables the caregivers and their crew to focus on the myriad physical details of healing, and Hashem is hopefully orchestrating the heavenly *refuah*.

SICKNESS IS DEBILITATING IN ALL AREAS OF LIFE. Hospitals, nursing homes and rehabilitation facilities each serve their functions, but in my mind, there is

The Home Backdrop for Healing

no place like home for healing. A friend who was undergoing a painful medical challenge with his wife, moving from one rehabilitation facility to another, commented about the environment that he saw in the home: "I saw the house was filled with *simchah!*" Illness brings so much pain to *all* family members, and a morose, somber, melancholy atmosphere is hardly what is needed to help the ill person feel uplifted. Children, grandchildren and noise are important parts of life. They are part of *normal* life, with the vibrancy and energy that they exude. It's a reaffirmation to all members of the family, but most of all to the patient, that as much as humanly possible, we will keep the "normal" parts of life just as they are – normal!

One of my children made an interesting observation. Often, when one is physically compromised, they are treated that way. When one has difficulty hearing, someone speaking to him will naturally raise his voice to enable the person to hear them. When one is unable to speak at all, the visitor will sometimes change their tenor, almost speaking down to the one who is ill. Their hearing is not affected at all, but the subtleties of how they are spoken to may sometimes change as well. For children, this is their mother; to a husband, this is his wife; to friends, this is their companion for so many years. She is the same person whom they have always loved and certainly no less of a person; on the contrary, she is that much more. A human is comprised of their physical being and their spiritual self. The constant state of tension that exists throughout life, the *neshamah* seeking to elevate itself while the physical body tries to bring it down, is part of our lives as Jews. The less one is able to do in the realm of the physical, the greater they are in the world of spirit.

The Rambam's famous Prayer for the Physician underscores the way a doctor must view his patients, but the statement has universal lessons, for caregivers, friends and family members. "When I see a man in distress, let me see only a human being." We are our *neshamah*, the vestige of G-dliness that is the rest of our being. We are not defined by an illness, nor does any physical impediment detract from the way we should be perceived by others. The dignity of a human being is a precious gift to each of us, and one who is ill and must be cared for by others should be accorded an extra measure of sensitivity. When our loved one cannot communicate, the challenge is that much greater – and our responsibility to accord them *enhanced* feeling and caring will help *us* in the way we look at them at them and how they feel about themselves.

I FREELY ADMIT IT: I AM GUILTY OF FEELING GUILTY when it came to the care of my wife, *a"h*. How does one measure the

Jewish Guilt: Motivator or Detractor

time that should be spent with a spouse, a parent or child, often neglecting oneself, one's *parnassah*, and one's other children or family members? Does it matter if one is a man or a woman, being responsible to provide the livelihood for one's family, or is responsible for the needs of one's children? Is there a difference if the person is ill for a month, two years or ten years? Is the primary caregiver's role different if there are auxiliary family members who can take "shifts" and relieve him of some of the responsibility?

These are weighty questions, and no simple answers can be applicable in all situations. What does the patient want? What do they need? What is my role specifically – to talk, to read, to just be there for someone whom we love so much? Can I *ever* say that I have done enough for them? What would I want, if, *chalilah*, the roles were reversed? I recall speaking to someone who was visiting his sister, who was in a very advanced stage of her illness. He said something to her that could have been misconstrued as being insensitive to her condition, and he began to profusely apologize. In her weakened state she told him reassuringly; "My brother, I am *so* far beyond letting petty things or statements upset me! There is surely no need to apologize!"

This exalted spiritual demeanor does not absolve one from being particularly attuned to their compromised physical, emotional and psychological state. The compassion and care that should be accorded *every* person we meet is magnified when we are dealing with a loved one who because of illness seems to be different than they once were. It is incumbent upon caregivers primarily, as well as family and friends, to see past the diminished exterior to the true human being.

EVERYTHING IS FOUND IN THE TORAH. INTERPERSONAL relationships, our way of thinking and acting, care, sensitivity and

Torah Perspectives on Bikur Cholim

our social interactions all find their source in the Torah. The Torah in *parshas Vayeira* shares the story of Avraham Avinu, who was visited by Hashem, as it were, on the third day after his *bris milah*, when Avraham was 99 years old. Hashem made it exceedingly hot, so Avraham would not be disturbed by wayfarers whom he always invited into his home. Avraham went outside his tent to look for guests to invite, and Hashem sent three angels, dressed like Arab wayfarers, to travel toward Avraham's tent.

The verses are puzzling. There are no "first thoughts and changes of heart" in reference to the Almighty. If Hashem deemed it important that Avraham rest after his circumcision, He shouldn't have sent the messengers; if guests were of paramount importance to Avraham's emotional well-being, then why did Hashem make it exceedingly hot in the first place? The lesson to be learned from the Torah portion is of critical importance in the care of one who is ill. Hashem saw Avraham undergo circumcision at the age of 99, a procedure that would be taxing on someone a fraction of his age and in perfect health. The immediate need was for undisturbed rest and relaxation. When Hashem saw that the emotional discomfort over not having guests overrode Avraham's physical pain, He sent His heavenly messengers to alleviate his pain.

It is critical for the long-term caregiver – or a short-term visitor – to be constantly attuned to the changing needs of the sick individual. The subtle signs of change in condition are cues for the family and friends as to what can best help the infirm person *now*, at this moment. *A friend takes a few minutes from his or her busy schedule to visit someone who has undergone a procedure. The patient is excited to receive a visitor and awaits their arrival. After a few moments of chatting, the patient feels the effects of the procedure and begins to fade off into a much-needed, restful sleep. The patient desperately needed the visit – and then she desperately needed to sleep. The visit is over, as the visitor saw what her sick friend needed and left.*

Bikur cholim is not only fulfilled by visiting the sick. The word *bikur* is from the root word of *l'vakeir*, to search out. The mitzvah of *bikur cholim* is to find out what the *choleh* needs, *now* – and that need may change a few minutes into the visit. *Bikur cholim* means being there for the person in need to address that which he is lacking and responding to it wisely. Another poignant message from the *parshah* about *bikur cholim* regards the interchange between Hashem and Avraham when Hashem came to visit. "*Vayeira eilav Hashem b'Eilonei Mamrei*" – And Hashem appeared to him in Elonei Mamrei. Interestingly, the verses relate no dialogue whatsoever – because apparently there was none! The visit is made to determine the need, to demonstrate friendship and caring and to pray on behalf of the one who is ill. Words may not be necessary to show that you care – rather, what's important is being there to meet *his* or *her* need. That is the true essence of *bikur cholim*.

THE CAREGIVER FOR A LOVED ONE HAS THE DAUNTING task of being the "point person" to apprise individuals about how the

Public Pain/ Private Pain

patient is faring. Some polite inquirers merely wish to show their concern, and statements such as, "I am thinking of _____ and am *davening* for his/her recovery" are a welcome gesture. When one is not part of the ill person's inner circle, asking too many questions can be intrusive and burdensome. If someone asks, it is usually because they care enough, and a courteous response is in order. Hopefully, you will not be grilled about specific interventions, detailed information or areas that should be reserved for family and very close friends.

In our own insular community, there are very few secrets, particularly when a family is challenged by illness. Names of the ill are inevitably added to Tehillim lists, and the private lives of family members often become part of the public arena. How does the caregiver walk the delicate communal tightrope, protecting the privacy of the ill family member – and himself – while still maintaining his or her social standing? No one wants to always wear pain on their sleeve, nor do they want to convey an attitude that everything is fine, when indeed it may not be.

I recall once that it must have been a particularly difficult day, and a community member took me to task – for displaying my true emotions for him to see! Rav Yisroel Salanter's statement about a person's face being a *reshus harabim*, public domain, rang so true. My face, my *panim*, revealed my *penim*, my innermost being – and this individual was not pleased by what he saw! I felt uncomfortable; how could I balance my external demeanor with my inner turmoil, being considerate of others while being honest with myself?

I expressed my concerns to the Mashgiach of the Mirrer Yeshiva, Rav Ezriel Erlanger, *shlita,* son-in-law of the famed *ba'al mussar*, Rav Shlomo Wolbe, *zt"l.* In his role as Mashgiach, I felt he could share insights on this emotional juggling act. There was another reason I thought the Mashgiach could relate to my situation. The Mashgiach's *rebbetzin* was also compromised for years by a physical ailment, and

I thought that perhaps the Mashgiach could share an insight that would be helpful.

I wasn't disappointed. The Mashgiach, *shlita,* pointed to a phrase quoted by *Chovos Halevavos* in chapter four of *Sha'ar Haperishus.* While the specific subject of Rabbeinu Bachye's words dealt with an individual and how he conducts himself in a world of excess and indulgence, the message resonated with me greatly. *Tzahala b'fanav v'aveilo b'libo* – one can exhibit joy on his face yet carry pain in his heart! This simple, empowering statement gives us direction on how a Yid can live his life. The public persona doesn't have to be in conflict with one's inner dimension; on the contrary – one can live in two worlds simultaneously. To the outside world, one exhibits contentment and serenity. There is a medical protocol, there are *tefillos* recited by family and friends, and everything that can be done for our loved one is being done. Yet inside, we feel the pain. The nagging questions about prognoses and cure, comfort and wellbeing, the day-to-day challenges and the long-term concerns are part of our daily existence.

I drew a parallel from a fascinating *halachah* about a year when the ninth day of Av falls on Shabbos. The actual observance of Tishah B'Av, the fasting, the *kinnos,* the feelings of *aveilus,* are pushed off until Sunday. The *Mechaber (siman 552)* instructs us on how to comport ourselves on Shabbos itself when it is prohibited to exhibit mourning or display sadness. During the *seudah shelishis,* toward the end of Shabbos, we conduct ourselves in an almost festive manner, having a *seudah* "like King Solomon during the time of his reign." We can imagine the way that meal must have been celebrated; no food or delicacy was withheld. The same is true for this last meal on Shabbos that is actually the ninth of Av – it is Shabbos and there can be no display of mourning. Yet, the *Mishnah Berurah* says that the tone of this festive Shabbos *seudah* **is** different: "Nonetheless, one must sit with sadness in his *nefesh.*" Our external actions are in concert with the celebration of Shabbos, a lavish Shabbos, but simultaneously, we are enjoined to let our *neshamos* feel the pain of Tishah B'Av. We can exhibit two emotions – totally contradictory – at one time, for that is our power as a Yid. At times it's a difficult challenge to show a face that's so different from our inner feelings, but it's a *gevurah,* an internal strength that allows us to be there for our loved one – and to be there for ourselves.

KEY POINTS:

- As a person matures, his sense of "self" grows to include important people in his life. When caring for a close relative, this expanded sense of self allows one to see the patient's needs as his own.

- Developing *emunah peshutah* – uncomplicated faith – is a lifelong process. It is something that must be nurtured in the years before the onset of an illness.

- When a family member is ill, it is often necessary to reconcile oneself to the role of taker, even when one has spent years giving to others.

- There is no place like home for healing. Even with an ill person in the home, the family should try to maintain as many normal aspects of the household as possible.

- When a loved one is compromised and/or cannot communicate, we need to remember to treat them with more dignity, not less. This will affect how we look at them and how they feel about themselves.

- There are no simple answers regarding how much time and effort should be expended on behalf of the ill person.

- It is critical for the long-term caregiver to be attuned to the changing needs of the patient.

- *Bikur cholim* does not only mean visiting the sick. It is a mitzvah that is fulfilled by determining what the patient is lacking and responding to that need wisely.

- If someone asks about the ill person, it's usually because they really care, and a courteous answer is appropriate.

- When struggling with uncertainty, fear, etc., as a caregiver, one should still try to display a pleasant face to the world. It can be challenging to show a face so different from what one is feeling internally, but that strength allows one to carry on.

Pondering those Precious Moments Before Parting Ways

Rabbi Eytan Feiner

I T WAS *EREV* YOM KIPPUR, AND THE FEAR AND trepidation of the impending day seized one and all, especially those in proximity of the awe-inspiring Brisker Rav. And yet, none other than the uniquely devout *rav* himself summoned his disciple Yechiel Michel Feinstein to accompany him on a walk through the neighboring streets. Yechiel Michel could not contain his astonishment, humbly inquiring from his *rebbi* why the Brisker Rav felt the need for a stroll just hours before the holiest day of the year. With the Day of Atonement looming, is there any more crucial time to squeeze in a little more Torah, *tefillah*, Tehillim… *teshuvah?* But a walk around town – now?!

Addressing his student's query, the always-calculated *rav* responded along the following lines: "My doctor instructed me to walk every day to best preserve my health. If I jettison the necessary walk to learn another *blatt Gemara*, recite more Tehillim, etc., then yes, I will be immersed in wonderful *mitzvos* before the great day arrives. But I will not be entering Yom Kippur having done the *ratzon Hashem* (will of Hashem). If the Torah dictates that we must do our utmost to guard our health, then I must heed my doctor's advice and close the Gemara, put down the *sefer Tehillim* and opt instead to follow HaKaddosh Baruch Hu's mandate of *"vi'nishmartem me'od*

Rabbi Eytan Feiner currently serves as the rav of Congregation Kneseth Israel, more popularly known as The White Shul, in Far Rockaway, New York. He also delivers monthly shiurim at Lander's Yeshiva, lectures extensively throughout the New York area and beyond, and is the summer rabbi of Chai Lifeline's Camp Simcha.

l'nafshoseichem" (guarding one's health very carefully). That is the very best way to go into Yom Kippur – knowing full well that I did not do what *I* wished most to do, but acted in the way HaKaddosh Baruch Hu wanted me to act."

A brief vignette in the annals of the illustrious Brisker dynasty – and one that conveys a powerful message indeed. No matter the day, the time, the particular occasion on hand: of paramount importance is the cognizance that a Jew must constantly focus on what Hashem wants from him at every moment in time. At the forefront of our mind must always be the question, "What does the Ribbono Shel Olam want me to be doing right now?" Are we relentlessly pursuing, "*batel retzoncha mipnei ritzono (Avos 2:4)* – nullify your will before His will," or do we turn the spotlight on what makes us feel good and what makes us feel holy? True piety demands shifting the focus away from selfish – albeit noble – pursuits and turning our concern toward what the Torah and our *gedolim* teach us is the will of Hashem in every scenario that life sends our way.

Another great anecdote with a similar potent message to be gleaned: The son of the Chafetz Chayim was once sitting on a train in Europe alongside the son of a renowned Chassidic *rebbe*. The *rebbe's* son turned to his seatmate and proudly proclaimed that he lived in a home wherein his father's otherworldly blessings and ensuing miracles were readily apparent; this was an environment in which "*tzaddik gozer v'HaKaddosh Baruch Hu mekayeim*" (a righteous person decrees and Hashem fulfills it) reverberated throughout.

After listening quietly and attentively, the Chafetz Chayim's son responded: "In our home, I witness daily just the opposite – whatever HaKaddosh Baruch Hu is *gozer* (decrees), the Chafetz Chayim is *mekayeim* (fulfills)! Whatever Hashem demands and decrees, my saintly father does his utmost to fulfill." The holy Chafetz Chayim unremittingly subjugated his will to the will of the One Above. And that is an even higher level.

WHAT, THEN, IS THE WILL OF HASHEM WHEN ONE FINDS himself at the bedside of a terminally ill patient, in the room with

At the *Choleh's* Bedside

a family member or friend whose demise is imminent? Should one be reciting Tehillim incessantly – after all, written with *ruach hakoddesh*, David HaMelech's monumental work has the Divine resonating in every line – or should you perhaps inquire more deeply into what the ill person himself really wishes for at that specific moment?

Rav Moshe Feinstein explains that the mitzvah of *bikur cholim* is thus labeled because this mitzvah requires, first and foremost, a genuine act of *"bikur."* The word does not simply translate into a mere visit; rather, just as *"**bikur** hakorban"* means intensely inspecting an animal to ensure it is free of all blemishes, so does **bikur** *cholim* connote an earnest and sincere scrutiny into all the disparate needs of the *choleh*. Yes, of course, one ought to take out a *sefer Tehillim* and fervently recite David's masterful collection of heart-wrenching and heaven-ascending psalms. At the right time. But first things first: what does the patient truly yearn for at this very moment, right here and right now? Perhaps a listening ear, or perhaps to hear you sing a soothing *niggun* or share a *geshmake vort* or an inspiring story… Or maybe just to hold tightly and securely onto his hand and let him really feel that *"nafsh'cha keshura b'nafsho* (your soul is bound with his soul)."

Sometimes one doesn't need to say anything at all. A bereaved family was most consoled by Rav Chayim Shmuelevitz, the famed Mirrer Rosh Yeshivah, when he came to comfort the mourners and simply sat and cried along with them without ever uttering a single word. Sit close. Hold on tight. Look lovingly and caringly into the *choleh*'s eyes. Perhaps allow the genuine tears to flow freely. And let the *choleh* know that you are with him at this delicate moment, fully engaged in a profound connection of two *neshamos* as you do your utmost to feel his emotions as best you can.

Oh, but how I yearn to do something "holy" – how I pine to feverishly recite the precious words of Tehillim, to complete the entire *sefer* over and over again on the ill person's behalf… A praiseworthy pursuit indeed. At the right place and at just the right time. Most often, however, the first course of action is to put the Tehillim down and allow the person to guide you – with words or perhaps a mere look in his eyes; through those windows into the recesses of his soul, you will discover what it is that he would appreciate most to truly be there with him at this somber time.

AS I WRITE, I CAN'T HELP BUT RECALL WHEN OUR DEAR son, Avraham Yeshayahu, was born, and we spent the larger part of

A Personal Reflection

his first year in various ICUs together with him. It was Shavuos time when we found ourselves in the pediatric ICU at Haddasah Ein Kerem in Yerushalayim, and the *yom tov* was winding down as I neared my goal of finishing reviewing a certain *masechta*. Sitting by the bedside of my adorable but very ill son and sensing the sun's setting, I was about to get up and complete the last few pages of the Gemara in solitude, when I peered yet again into his beautiful eyes. Those precious eyes indicated instantly that this *heilige neshamah* before me wanted nothing more in the world than to be picked up and held tightly as Shavuos neared its close.

So I put the Gemara down and gently picked up my son – tubes, wires and all – and in place of learning from the Torah in the waning moments of *yom tov*, I danced in place in an ICU while holding my pure and pristine son, my little holy *"Sefer Torah,"* and singing him a Torah *niggun* from the depths of my soul. And we shed tears together as one.

Perhaps in line with the Brisker Rav, at times we need to ask ourselves what is the true will of Hashem in this particular instance. How I would have loved to finish that *masechta* on *Zeman Mattan Toraseinu*. But that Shavuos a *choleh* – my very own son – really needed me. And that meant gently putting the Gemara aside and cradling this gentle soul in its place – to be there for him, with him… and, as I look back pensively, what a meaningful and memorable Shavuos it was and will forever be.

YEARS AGO, I HAD THE PRIVILEGE OF LEARNING WITH A remarkable young man, a *yeshivah bachur* by the name of Moishe.

A Special Place, A Remarkable Person

The setting was in Chai Lifeline's Camp Simcha, where I have the *zechus* to serve as a *rav* in the summer, to teach and learn Torah with both staff and campers. I had a daily *chavrusa* with Moishe, a holy and radiant soul whose body was tragically stricken with cancer; he was told that he didn't have much time left to live. His final dream in this world, his last wish? No, he turned down the trips, the computers, the gadgets, the material and the mundane – all he craved was a set of *Shas*, a longing easily surpassed by the desire to finish it before he passed away.

We often learned together outdoors, as Moishe enjoyed delving deeply into HaKaddosh Baruch Hu's Torah while surrounded by the scenic backdrop of a beautiful lake and trees, enveloped by the embracing warmth of the summer sun. He wished to study the ultimate *"niflaòs haBorei* (wonders of the Creator)" of the eternal Torah against a background of the *niflaòs haBorei* ingrained in the natural world.

But one day he failed to show up. And boy did I get nervous. Eventually I did find him in the infirmary, but not because he needed to be there at the time for medical reasons. This same pious Moishe – a *bachur* about whom the *gadol hador*, Rav Chayim Kanievsky, *shlita*, declared after conversing with him that "he is not from this world" – was filming a fun music video in the hallway of the camp's infirmary! What in the world could be going on?! His only goal in the short time he had remaining in this world was to finish all of *Shas*, and, lo and behold, here he was in the midst of a music video...

Noticing my surprise and utter disbelief, Moishe explained that, indeed, his lifelong passion was Torah and his dream was *Shas*. But upon being informed that his fellow campers – especially those confined to the infirmary – would get much *chizzuk v'idud*, strength and encouragement, from watching the budding *talmid chacham* and *ben aliyah* sing and dance in a camp video, he readily acquiesced. *Shas* was top priority and the love of his life. But here he was in a camp together with many ill campers afflicted with myriad ailments who would get great *chizzuk* if, just once, he would put his cherished Gemara aside and help create a music memento that would provide continued strength and uplift the spirits of so many of his fellow campers.

Well, dear Moishe, *z"l*, you most certainly uplifted mine. And you're in great company. The Brisker Rav enlightened us: sometimes we have to temporarily close the Gemara to take care of our health because doing the *ratzon Hashem* reigns supreme. And sometimes we have to close that same cherished Gemara (or tear-soaked Tehillim) to elevate the souls of those who are in need of our care and assistance. To be in the moment together with them, for them. In those precious moments before we part ways with someone whose life is passing before us, take the time to ponder – deeply and carefully – what the

Ribbono Shel Olam wants you to do, not for yourself, but for others –
and ultimately for Him.

KEY POINTS:

- A Jew must constantly focus on what Hashem wants from him at that moment in time.

- True piety demands shifting the focus from what we may feel is the right thing to do to that which the Torah and our *rabbanim* teach us is the will of Hashem.

- *Bikur cholim* means determining what the patient wants and needs most right now – whether it be a listening ear, a soothing song, a Torah thought, an inspiring story, etc.

- Sometimes no words need to be shared with the ill person; one can do more by demonstrating through eye contact or a tightly held hand that you are truly with him.

- Realize when it is appropriate to close the *sefer* or Tehillim, although it might feel more holy to be learning or *davening*, and rather be in the moment with the ill person.

Bringing an End to Galus Edom

Rabbi Aryeh Zev Ginzberg

NUMEROUS ARTICLES HAVE BEEN WRITTEN ON the topic of *kavod hameis*, many from this author, about the significance of the sanctity of life and of the requirement to prolong one's life, regardless of the level of functionality of that life.

We often quote the *Chazal*, "*Yafah sha'ah achas b'Olam Hazeh, mikol chayei Olam Haba* – greater is one hour of life in this world, than an eternity in the next world." *Chazal* refer to the opportunity to accomplish, gain *zechuyos*, and do *chessed* for others that cannot be done in the Heavenly world.

Most of us are familiar with the famous story of the Vilna Gaon, who was on his deathbed and began to cry. His students questioned his crying and said, "*Rebbi*, how can you cry when you are heading to a *lichtige Gan Eden* in reward for all that you accomplished in this world?"

The Vilna Gaon grabbed hold of the strings of his *tzitzis* and lovingly kissed them and said to them, "How can I not cry when I will soon be leaving the world that is so filled with *mitzvos* that by just putting on a four-cornered garment with *tzitzis* one fulfills a mitzvah in the Torah?"

And so, when I was first asked to write once again about the topic of *kavod hameis*, I declined because what else can I add to what has already been said and written? That was my decision until the incredible timing of a phone call changed my perspective and made me realize how very important this issue of *kavod hameis* is.

Rabbi Aryeh Zev Ginzberg is the rav of the Chofetz Chaim Torah Center of Cedarhurst and the founding rav of Ohr Moshe Institute in Hillcrest, Queens. He is a published author of several sifrei halachah and a frequent contributor to many magazines and newspapers, where he writes the Torah hashkafah on timely issues of the day. He is also a sought-after lecturer on Torah hashkafah at a variety of venues around the country.

TWO WEEKS AGO, I PARTICIPATED IN A PROGRAM FOR 500 Jewish university students, most of whom are either totally unaffiliated or marginally affiliated. It was a one-day forum, entitled, "The Resiliency of the Jewish People." The dedicated organizers of this program had divided it into two parts.

Cremation – Then and Now

The morning session would host several speakers, each focusing on a different historical period of *Churban* for the Jewish people that had lasting ramifications.

There was a session on the *Churban Beis Hamikdash* and the Jews going into *galus*; another on the Spanish Inquisition; and a third on the Holocaust.

The second part, held in the afternoon, would focus on the historical periods of rebuilding following the *Churban*: one session on the Chashmona'im and yet another on the creation of the State of Israel in 1948.

I agreed to participate in this innovative program and was given an hour for my presentation on the *Churban HaBayis*. Immediately following my lecture, an acclaimed historian and author of the Holocaust period was slated to present the absolute horrific destruction and suffering that Klal Yisrael went through during this period. I decided to stay and listen to his presentation.

While his presentation was enlightening and informative, he went into graphic detail about the use of the crematoria by the Nazis, *yemach shemam*. From my vantage point of the stage, I looked out at the crowd of young students and saw many of them squirming in their seats, having to listen to the presenter's graphic descriptions. At first, while sitting there, I couldn't understand why he chose to speak about this particular aspect of the Holocaust in such detail and why I needed to hear it. Less than an hour later, I understood.

After his presentation, I left the forum and was in my car heading to my next appointment, when my phone rang. On the other end of the line was a dear friend, the expert and advocate for *kavod hameis*, a person who has dedicated his life to *chessed shel emes*, Rabbi Elchonon Zohn. With his organization, NASCK (The National Association of Chevra Kadisha), he, perhaps more than anyone else, has raised the issue of *kavod hameis* to a place where it deserves to be, in the hearts and minds of every Jew.

The purpose of his call was to share with me another one of his creative ideas to help spread the idea of the importance of *kavod hameis* to the non-traditional Jewish communities. He then shared with me an astounding statistic that totally overwhelmed me: in certain Jewish communities around the country, the rate of Jewish families that choose cremation instead of burial is almost 70%! Nationally, it is about 40%. I was shocked, as I am sure that you are, at the level of disregard for our most sacred *mesorah* of burying our dead in the same manner that our *Avos Hakedoshim* did from the beginning of time.

After concluding the call, I couldn't ignore the coincidence of the timing of this call. I had just sat through an hour-long lecture on the horrific fate of Klal Yisrael in the Holocaust, which emphasized that even after all the colossal suffering and murder of millions of Yidden, the Nazis robbed their victims of the opportunity to be buried with *kevuras Yisrael* and instead burned their holy bodies in the crematoria.

And immediately afterward, I receive this phone call from Rabbi Zohn about the painful statistic of how many Yidden today, in a free country, in a *medinah shel chessed,* **choose** to do to their loved ones what the Nazis did to our parents and grandparents just decades ago.

It was at that moment that I decided to take pen in hand and once again reach out to *acheinu Bnei Yisrael* to take this issue very much to heart and let everyone do their part to increase the awareness of the value of life in this world and the significance of *kavod hameis* for those who have left this temporal world.

MANY MONTHS AGO, A VERY WONDERFUL MAN FROM the Five Towns community reached out to me with a painful *shailah.*

A Difficult Shailah His father had unfortunately suffered a major stroke more than a year ago and was in a comatose state ever since. Months earlier, he was transferred to a facility that was about an hour's drive from his son's home. For the first few months, the son visited his father every single day after leaving work and before going home. Eventually, he began limiting his visits to once a week, and lately, he had been going every other week.

The *shailah* that he asked me was a difficult and painful one. He explained that his father was in a coma and had no knowledge on any level that his son was there to visit him. The son had a very full day with a large, growing family at home, and each visit, which is an hour's travel time each way, would take more than two-and-a-half hours out of his already hectic day, leaving him physically and emotionally drained. Yet he felt terrible that he was not providing the proper *kibbud av,* and the infrequency of his visits to his father was greatly troubling him.

His *shailah* to me was: what was his requirement to his father under these circumstances and how often should he go? He made it very clear that he would follow whatever I instructed him to do.

I am sure that my rabbinic colleagues reading this also share my uneasiness in *paskening* this type of *shailah.* On one hand, *kibbud av* is a great mitzvah and is not meant to be easy to perform. On the other hand, the son's responsibility to his own family and his personal wellbeing were of paramount importance as well. I took the easy way out and told him I would consult with Harav Dovid Feinstein, *shlita,* and get back to him in a few days.

Combatting the Zechus of Edom

A FEW DAYS LATER, A FRIEND, RABBI BINYAMIN KOVAL, the Rosh Kollel of the Flatbush Morning Kollel, shared with me the most incredible insight that he had heard in the name of the then-*zakein hador,* Hagaon Harav Aharon Leib Shteinman, *zt"l,* that will be life-changing for many.

An elderly Yid was approaching his 100th birthday, and he was greatly troubled. He told his son, "I need to understand why I am *zocheh* to have this *arichus yamim.* My father died at 46 and his father before him at 41. I am a simple person, not learned or accomplished. Why am I *zocheh* to live now until the age of 100 (and beyond)?"

The son decided to present the *shailah* to the *gadol hador* Rav Shteinman to receive guidance on what he could answer his father. What the Rosh Yeshivah answered was absolutely incredible, and it could only come from someone whose vision of the happenings in this world, big or small, is worlds apart from our own.

The Rosh Yeshivah responded, "Tell your father the following reason why he is *zocheh* to *arichas yamim.* HaKaddosh Baruch Hu is working to bring an end to *Galus Edom.* The *zechus* that Edom had all these years was the great *kibbud av* that Esav had for his father. And so, Hashem, in the *tekufah acharonah,* was *meshaneh teva ha'olam* [changed the nature of the world], allowing people to live longer. Klal Yisrael, in caring for their elders longer, can generate additional *zechuyos* of *kibbud av,* which will be *k'negged* the *zechus* of Edom, thereby allowing us to (finally) bring an end to *Galus Edom."*

In other words, this person was *zocheh* to *arichas yamim* so that more *zechuyos* could be generated by his children and added to the collective *zechuyos* of Klal Yisrael.

What an absolutely incredible insight into the ways of the world! What our simple eyes see as the good fortune of growing old is really part of Hashem's plan to bring the *geulah* for Klal Yisrael.

After hearing this idea, I quickly called the fellow who asked me the *shailah* about his father and shared it with him. I suggested that he should keep the Rosh Yeshivah's insight in mind when trying to determine what his course of action should be in juggling his obligation to be with his father and his obligation to himself and his growing family.

This person called me again several months later. He had just gotten up from the *shivah* for his father, but wanted to express his *hakaras hatov* to me. He explained that ever since I shared with him the thought of Rav Aharon Leib, he once again began to visit his father several times a week.

However, those times he wasn't burdened with wondering what good his visits were accomplishing when his father was not even aware of his presence. Instead, every time he got into his car for the hour's drive to his father, he had in mind that he was contributing to bringing the end to *Galus Edom.* This so motivated him that he went enthusiastically, and it invigorated his family as well, as they all supported his efforts not only on their behalf, but on behalf of all of Klal Yisrael!

There you have it. It's all interconnected. *Kavod hameis* and *kavod hachai* should be viewed by us not as burdensome or insignificant, *chas v'Shalom*, but rather, as bringing an end to this bitter *galus* that we are in, one *zechus* at a time.

May it happen speedily in our day.

This article is written l'zecher nishmas Sarah Chaya bas Reb Aryeh Zev, a"h.

This article originally appeared in Hamodia and is reprinted here with their permission and that of the author.

KEY POINTS:

- While many of us recognize the sanctity of life and requirement to prolong life no matter the functionality of that life, we might feel there is nothing more to add to the topic.

- In shocking disregard for *kavod hameis,* in some communities in the United States, 70% of Jewish families choose cremation over burial! Nationally, about 40% of Jews choose cremation.

- The *zechus* that Edom has had all these years of *Galus Edom* is the great *kibbud av* Esav displayed toward his father Yitzchak. Now, Hashem is allowing people to live longer so that we can generate additional *zechuyos* of *kibbud av* to combat Edom's *zechus.*

- *Kavod hameis* and *kavod hachai* should not be viewed by us as burdensome, but rather, as a way to hasten the *geulah.* When caregiving and visiting an elderly or ill parent is done with this mindset, it can feel less burdensome to both the caregiver and his/her family.

CHAPTER II

Practical Guidance for the Caregiver

The Art of Being a Caregiver

Rabbi Moshe Meir Weiss

THE ROLE OF CAREGIVER IS CERTAINLY NOT ONE WE request. Undoubtedly, it is a very daunting and challenging responsibility. At the same time, it is a sublime opportunity that involves the lofty mitzvah of *v'halachta bidrachav*, walking in Hashem's ways. As we say in *Shemoneh Esreih*, Hashem is *mechalkel chayim b'chessed*, He sustains life with kindness. Similarly, David HaMelech says in Tehillim, *"v'Atah mechayeh es kulam"* – and You (Hashem) sustain everyone.

A Unique Mitzvah

If you are a caregiver for a parent, then at every moment, you are also fulfilling the Fifth Commandment of *kabbed es avicha v'es imecha*, honoring your father and mother. This mitzvah includes *ma'achil, u'mashkeh, malbish u'mechaseh, machnis u'motzi*, feeding them, giving them drink, helping them get dressed, and helping them in their comings and goings. These are all duties of a caregiver. This occupation comes with the Biblical promise of *l'ma'an yitav lach ul'ma'an ya'arichun yamecha*, in order that it should be good for you, and you should have length of days. The Fifth Commandment is included on the first tablet of the *Luchos*, which contains the *mitzvos* between man and Hashem. It is placed there because there are three partners in the creation of man: Hashem, the father and the mother. Hashem tells us, "I'm the silent partner. If you show honor to your father and mother, I will know that you honor Me as well."

If a husband is caring for a wife, he is living up to the commitment he made to her in the *kesubah*, when he pledged that he will *"okir, ezon, va'afarnes,"* cherish, feed, and support her. If a wife is caring for her husband, she is fulfilling her life's duty as an *ezer k'negdo*, acting as a helper for him. And when parents have the weighty and sad task of

---

Rabbi Moshe Meir Weiss is the rav of Agudath Israel of Staten Island. A popular writer and lecturer, his Torah column appears weekly in The Jewish Press.

caring for a sick or special child, they are living up to the expectations that Hashem has for them by granting them this child to bring into the world.

Hashem Has Confidence in Us

IT IS NORMAL FOR ANY CAREGIVER TO INITIALLY FEEL very overwhelmed. This job is, after all, often a 24/7 obligation, many times with no sign of light at the end of the tunnel. We must first be fortified with the awareness that, *ein HaKaddosh Baruch Hu ba betrunya im haberiyos* – Hashem doesn't ask us to take on more than we can handle. This is also the belief behind our national proclamation of *na'aseh venishma*, we will do and we will listen. This affirms that we believe we can tell Hashem that we will do whatever He commands even before we hear what it is because if Hashem tells us to do it, it is certainly something that we can handle.

Another thought that is helpful to consider when one is a long-term caregiver is that the Torah teaches us that the reward for honoring parents is *arichas yamim* (long life). The Torah almost never offers a specific reward for a mitzvah. The Rishonim explain that by doing so, the Torah is giving us *chizzuk* (encouragement) not to be dismayed if many of life's opportunities seem to pass us by because we are caring for somebody. Don't be discouraged by the fact that you're stuck in the house, that you miss *simchos*, that you can't spend more time with friends or visit relatives. Hashem is telling us, "I'll make it up to you and lengthen your life so that you will recover all the time that you missed out on."

A caregiver should remember the ways of Hashem, namely *middah k'neged middah*, that Hashem always treats us measure for measure. If we are there in someone's time of need, Hashem will be there for us when we need Him. David HaMelech teaches us, "*Ashrei maskil el dal b'yom ra'ah yemalteihu Hashem*," fortunate is one who acts wisely with one who is in need, as Hashem will save them from an evil day.

Refuas Hanefesh – Ensuring a Positive Outlook

IN THE *MI SHEBEIRACH* WE SAY AT *KRI'AS HATORAH* FOR one who is ill, we ask that Hashem grant them a *refuas hanefesh* and a *refuas haguf*, a healing for their soul and for their body. It is enormously important to note that we first request a *refuas hanefesh*, healing of the soul. A caregiver must pay special attention to the mental state of their charge. With this in mind, I believe fervently that one should make an initial assessment about whether the patient needs to know their specific diagnosis. If the one who is ill is not actively quarterbacking their own medical affairs, it is often a great kindness to spare them the grim finality of their medical predicament. Sometimes with the assistance of the medical team, a slight adjustment to their diagnosis can make the difference between having hope or living with crushing despair. For example, when my father, Aron Tzvi *ben* R' Meir took ill with pancreatic cancer, with the agreement of his doctors, I told my father that he had pancreatitis, a condition that mirrors most of the symptoms of pancreatic cancer. Until two weeks before he passed away, he lived with hope and not with the fear of imminent death.

This course of action is not for everyone. There are many who want to know every detail of their situation. Some people want to know how much time they have left. They want to make videos for their family, write ethical wills, and grab every available moment to do what they think is most important. This issue is so important that it behooves the caregiver to take counsel with a knowledgeable *rav* about whether to share a frightening diagnosis with the patient.

It is also important, as much as is possible, to give the patient as much hope as you can. When caring for someone with a specific disease, try to find another person who battled it successfully and have them visit your patient to give them encouragement. When choosing a doctor, since we believe that *refuas hanefesh*, the mental health of a person, is of paramount importance, make sure you find a doctor who has a good bedside manner, is optimistic, and doesn't alarm patients unnecessarily. This choice can make the difference between life and death. When choosing a doctor, it is also important to determine his general availability. The fact that a doctor is from the top twenty-five in the world will be of little benefit if you can't call him or her if the patient has sudden pain or fear or there is a new development.

Here's an important piece of advice for those caring for a patient with cancer: besides finding a qualified, warm and sensitive oncologist, it's of great importance to have a very good internist. Often, a person fighting cancer does not suffer from their immediate cancer. Rather, the cancer and its associated treatments unfortunately break down the body, and other areas of health are affected. Treating these issues is not within the specific expertise of the specialized oncologist. For example, a skilled internist will be better equipped in how to deal with side effects such as constipation, heartburn or joint pains.

One of the ways of positively impacting the patient's mental wellbeing is by discovering how, in the *choleh*'s incapacitated state, they can still experience pleasure. For some, this means surrounding them with happy music. Others who are more delicate and cannot tolerate noise find aromatherapy to be uplifting. Remember that the sense of the soul is smell. That's why we make a *berachah* on the *besamim* right after Shabbos, to console us for the loss of the *neshamah yeseirah* (extra Shabbos soul). Yet others are boosted by a massage. There are those who are uplifted by listening to Torah lectures. Perhaps a big screen with Torah Anytime will give them a sense of meaning and value, even when they are confined to their sickbed.

ORCHESTRATE PACED VISITS FROM LOVING RELATIVES and good friends. Remember that as a caregiver, it is your responsibility

Helpful Visits, Harmful Visits

to be a traffic cop when it comes to visitors. Stagger the visits. Often, everyone comes on Shabbos afternoon, when it is convenient. The living room becomes full, and to the patient's frustration, everyone ends up talking to one another. Furthermore, during the rest of the week, no one comes to visit. So the first rule of thumb is make a schedule and limit the number of people at each specific time. Also, especially if the patient is unaware of the diagnosis, caution visitors about this before they come into the house.

Familiarize yourself with who is a healing visitor and who aggravates or irritates the patient. The art of *bikur cholim* (visiting the sick) is not for everyone. I'll give you a simple example. When the sick person asks, "Do they miss me at work?" the uninitiated will answer, "Don't worry. Everything is fine." Actually, that's the worst thing to say. The sick person sinks deeper into the bed thinking, "They don't even miss me. It makes no difference that I'm not there." The intelligent visitor will proclaim, "We are barely surviving without you. We can't wait to have you back." Discourage visits from people who make comments like, "For someone with your sickness, you don't look too bad," or "*Baruch Hashem*, you can catch up on your reading." It's amazing what comes out of the mouths of mindless visitors. People have been overheard telling the suffering person, "Don't worry! If something happens to you, I'll be there for you and your family." Also, know how deflect the know-it-alls or alternative medicine cultists who want to tell you all the things you should be doing, pushing their own agendas and advising that you stop seeing mainstream professionals. Surround the patient with optimistic people who are not there for themselves, but who come to gladden and enrich the life of the one who is suffering.

The mental health of the patient is also strengthened when you obtain blessings for them from *gedolim* and inform them that people are praying for them at the *Kosel* and *kivrei tzaddikim* (graves of the righteous). Hearing that friends are regularly saying Tehillim for them is also encouraging. So is knowing that people are giving *tzeddakah* or performing other *mitzvos* as a merit for their speedy recovery.

In general, it is a great balm for the patient to know that they have friends who are thinking of them. I have always wondered why the Hebrew word for friend, *rei'echa,* shares the same *shoresh* (root word) as *ra,* evil! After all, one of life's greatest treasures is a good friend. Good times are doubled when you have a friend to share them with, and troubles are halved when you have a friend to commiserate with you. I think the answer is that you can tell who your friends really are in "bad" times, hence the connection to the word *ra.* Fair-weather friends disappear when times are tough, but true friends are really there for you when things get choppy.

IT IS OBVIOUS THAT TO MAINTAIN THE PATIENT'S MENTAL health, the caregiver has to help their charge be as pain-free as possible.

Managing Pain This can be a daunting task when dealing with something as thorny as cancer breakout pain. However, with today's sophisticated medicine, there should be no reason for the *choleh* to be suffering in constant pain. *Baruch Hashem,* today we have a vast arsenal of painkillers available. From Percocet to slow-release morphine to fentanyl patches and sprays, you should be able to find a way to keep the pain under control. Of course, balancing the side-effects of these powerful drugs is another issue. Constipation can be a big problem. Even more serious is the balancing act between chasing away pain and enhancing the patient's quality of life, as opposed to consigning them to a sleepy, drug-hazed existence induced by too many pain meds. Even more serious is the real possibility of stopping a person's breathing by overmedicating.

For non-terminal conditions, there is also the serious specter of addiction, which needs to be considered. In hospitals such as Sloan-Kettering, the patient is assigned a pain-management specialist. In other cases, the oncologist might be an expert in this branch of medicine. And in some circumstances, the family has to bring in a specialist on their own. Either way, this is a quality-of-life issue of paramount importance that needs constant attention and may require frequent adjustments. There are times when the *choleh* gets used to a specific medicine and it needs to be changed. Other times there is a period of remission, and the meds can be significantly reduced. Also, be aware that the correct approach is often not achieved on the first attempt but rather, through trial-and-error and delicate calibration.

This is a good place to speak about proper medical insurance. Many pain medications are very, very expensive. Having a good insurance plan can make the difference in obtaining the most effective meds. Organizations such as RCCS might be able to help guide you regarding how to upgrade your insurance. A compassionate oncologist might also be able to get the patient on a program to receive sophisticated painkillers or he/she might be able to offer samples to help out. Good insurance is critical in many other ways, such as in obtaining approval for immunotherapies and helpful testing.

It is also important to use an oncologist with ethical integrity. Unfortunately, economics can dictate medical decisions if the physician is greedy. Changing a patient's chemo regimen when the cancer markers are skyrocketing can mean losing data for a profitable study. Moving a patient off chemotherapy to some immunotherapy drugs might be beneficial to the patient but can significantly reduce the physician's profits.

IT IS NOT ONLY PAIN MEDS THAT DEMAND THE caregiver's attention. Sleep is imperative for healing and for the

Refuas Haguf – Physical Care

strength to fight diseases and tolerate treatment. But worries about the future, fear of treatments, surgery and pain, and of course, the pain itself can make sleeping very difficult. Sleeping pills can make a significant difference in the patient's quality of life. Sometimes the use of pain meds that also can make a person drowsy negates the need for sleeping aids. The interaction between the sleeping pills and pain meds will need to be monitored. Another point to be aware of is the sagacious usage of anti-depressants and anti-anxiety medicines. When someone is suffering from a dangerous or debilitating disease, they can become quite depressed or anxious. It is wise to have a proper psychiatric advisor assist in buoying the spirits of a suffering *choleh*.

One of the greatest responsibilities of a successful caregiver is ensuring that the patient receives proper nutrition. Often the disease or the treatments or both affect a person's appetite. At the same time, it is so important for the patient to receive proper nutrition. This involves finding high calorie foods that tickle the palate of the patient. It usually means providing them with small portions every two hours. It also means being very patient when offering food to the patient. Medical supplements such as Ensure and Sustecal can be helpful. For those who can't tolerate milk, Ensure Clear might be an option. Experimenting with different fruits, vegetables, and soups is highly recommended.

Frequently, treatments cause severe nausea. When my father, *a"h,* was ill, we visited an upscale candy store and bought a few of every type of candy. I had my father try all of them, and he found one chocolate candy that gave him relief from the nausea.

Sunlight is very helpful in lifting the spirits of a person. Whenever you can get your patient out and into the sun, do so. It is also a very big relief not to be cooped up in the house all the time. Exercise and fresh air is almost always just what the doctor ordered.

There is a strong temptation to run to the hospital at the slightest hint of an emergency. More often than not, the hospital is the worst place for a long-term patient. When a weakened person is hospitalized, they often stop eating (they are given nutrition intravenously), they stop going to the bathroom (they use a catheter), and they stop walking or even sitting. Sadly, after a long hospital stay, they might never regain the use of these physical mechanics. Try to resist the urge to run to the hospital unless, of course, there is real danger. Developing a relationship with specific Hatzolah members who are familiar with the case can be very helpful when making such a decision. Also, make sure to consult your main physician as to when you must absolutely drop everything and run to the hospital.

For many serious conditions, regular tests, such as CT scans and MRIs, are a part of life. They are very scary, for each one is like a mini *yom haDin* (day of judgment). The caregiver should make sure that the patient never goes to a scan alone. They should also try to fast-track the results of the testing for it can be very nerve-wracking to wait for the results. I once heard Rav Gifter, *zt"l, zy"a,* speak to a large group of doctors. He told them in no uncertain terms that if they know the results of a test before Shabbos it is criminal not to share them until after the weekend.

A caregiver must be careful not to become a jailer. Yes, it's normal to be super-worried about germs, as catching a cold or infection (a real worry since the immune system is compromised) could mean pausing treatment or a trip to the hospital. However, attending a *simchah* or a reunion or just visiting the grandchildren can inject light and meaning into a desperate situation. Compromising by having the *choleh* wear a nice pair of white gloves (if we are talking about a female) and agreeing not to hug and kiss people, as well as capping the visit so that it will not be too taxing, might be helpful options. Remember, there's nothing better for the patient's emotional wellbeing than giving them something to live for.

Caring for the Caregiver

SINCE CAREGIVING IS A 24/7 OCCUPATION, THE SMART caregiver needs to learn how to delegate often and wisely. Save your strength and time for when you are needed most. Never wait on line in CVS; ask eager friends to do that. Don't shop for the fresh avocado and cantaloupe; ask others to take care of that. If there are children, give them jobs to do; it is their privilege as taught in the Fifth Commandment. Accept assistance from *bikur cholim* and other organizations if necessary. Don't be shy about accepting offers of help. If the house isn't clean or the food isn't plentiful, the *choleh* and the whole family will suffer. Yidden need *zechusim*; let them help when there is a legitimate cause!

While the caregiver's thoughts are focused on the patient, they must remember to take care of themselves as well. One must maintain proper eating and sleeping habits in order to have strength to care for a loved one. Someone who is eager to help should be given the responsibility of providing food for the caregiver. Getting enough sleep can prove more challenging, since when someone is ill, their needs don't respect the clock. If possible, the approach is the same as a mother who takes care of an infant, namely, sleep when the patient sleeps. When this is not possible, a rotation of trained people should be requisitioned to spell the caregiver so they can get adequate sleep. Sometimes an aide can serve in this role. However, if there are life-threatening circumstances, it is likely that you won't want to rely on an unrelated secular aide. Included in taking care of oneself is the need to take a break and get away for a bit. The patient will be served better when the caregiver comes back refreshed and ready to be of assistance!

OFTEN, WHEN CARING FOR AN AGED PARENT, THE task falls on one child who is geographically available. If this is the case, the other children should

Caregiving and Family Relationships

make sure to pitch in often to give the primary caregiver a break. If the livelihood of the family who is doing the bulk of the caregiving is affected by their responsibilities, the other children should all contribute financially. In many cases, they would be permitted to use their *ma'aser* money for this purpose. In some situations, it is not a geographic or economic situation that dictates who becomes the primary caregiver, but simply that one of the children steps up to the plate while the others just don't! This can lead to a lot of hard feelings. The family who is doing the mitzvah should thank Hashem for the *zechus* rather than jeopardize family relationships. Sometimes the other relatives are not capable or their spouses are not willing. Hashem keeps the score and will reward those that help their flesh and blood in their time of need. Don't spoil the glorious mitzvah with sibling rivalry and negativity.

When bringing an aged or sick parent into one's home when you are living with other family members, there are unique challenges. One who is taking care of the parent needs to be careful not to neglect their spouse and/or children. The balancing act between the mitzvah of *kibbud av v'eim* and *shalom bayis* is indeed a delicate one. A *rav* should be consulted if the role of caregiver is infringing on one's *shalom bayis*. A similar tug of war can occur when caring for an aged parent while managing a household of children. Once again, a *rav* should be consulted for guidance if the children are acting out in resentment because of the necessary preoccupation with the needy parent.

IF THE PATIENT IS A SPOUSE, THERE CAN BE OTHER UNIQUE challenges. It is important for the caregiver to constantly reassure

Caring for a Spouse

their spouse that they are not a burden and that they still love them. If it is the wife who is ill, it's important to tell her that she is still beautiful. If there is hair loss because of chemo, this is especially important. Beautiful wigs and chic *tichels* and snoods can do wonders. Severe weight loss to the point of emaciation makes such protestations challenging, but Hashem gives us *siyata d'Shmaya* when we do the right thing. I have found it helpful to tell someone who is traumatized by chemo hair loss that they should think that every hair that comes out signifies that the disease is departing as well.

One specific challenge when caring for a spouse is that the caregiver might need to take on the role of disciplinarian. He or she has to ensure that their spouse receives proper nutrition, adequate sleep, necessary treatments, and avoids germs. The healthy spouse can become almost like a dictator. This can lead to a scary condition, which I have labeled "caregiver hostility," when a patient becomes angry and hostile to the caregiver spouse. This seems counterintuitive, since the caregiver is putting their life on hold to care for their spouse. But the patient feels scared and trapped and unhappy and transfers all this frustration onto the one who is "controlling" them. I have heard from a top oncological psychiatrist that this has actually resulted in many divorces. The best case in such a situation is for the caregiver to take a step back, bringing in others to give temporary support until the marital equilibrium is restored.

In *Rosh Chodesh bentching*, we ask Hashem for *chayim aruchim* (long life). Why don't we ask for *chayim shel chodesh* (life for a month), since in the next *Rosh Chodesh bentching* we will again ask for long life? A beautiful answer is that each month we are asking Hashem that we should feel no lumps, experience no dizziness, and suffer no scares that would threaten our knowledge that we have a long life ahead of us. May we and our loved ones be blessed with long life, good health, and everything wonderful.

KEY POINTS:

- Caregiving can be a fulfillment of various *mitzvos,* including, *v'halachta bidrachav,* (walking in Hashem's ways); *kibbud av v'eim,* (honoring one's parents); satisfying one's *kesubah* commitment to his wife; discharging one's obligations to her husband as an *ezer k'negdo.*

- Hashem does not ask us to do more than we can handle, and He pays back in kind those who help others in their time of need.

- The mental health of the patient is of paramount importance. Therefore, it is important to consider whether or not the patient needs to know the specifics of his diagnosis; to choose a doctor with a positive outlook and good bedside manner; to determine how to help the patient experience pleasure despite his compromised situation; to implement effective pain management.

- Be a traffic cop regarding visitors. Stagger visits. And try to weed out harmful visitors who aggravate the patient.

- Physical care for an ill patient includes managing their pain; ensuring adequate sleep and nutrition; determining the need for psychiatric care to help with anxiety and/or depression; incorporating exercise and fresh air when possible.

- Know when it is really necessary to bring a patient to the hospital – and when it's not.

- Ensure that the patient never goes for a scan or diagnostic test alone.

- Allowing the patient to join in a *simchah* or family occasion with reasonable parameters to protect their health can be beneficial for their emotional well-being.

- Your welfare as a caregiver is very important. Therefore, you should not hesitate to accept outside help and delegate responsibilities whenever possible. Do whatever it takes to maintain proper eating and sleeping habits in order to have the strength to care for your loved one.

- While it is proper for siblings to assist and relieve the primary caregiver often, when this does not occur, thank Hashem for the *zechus* you have, rather than jeopardize family relationships.

- Be careful not to neglect your spouse and/or children when caregiving and consult with a *rav* whenever necessary to find the correct balance.

- When caring for a spouse, be careful to reassure them that they are not a burden and are very much loved.

- If the patient feels "controlled" by the caregiving spouse, it might be necessary to bring in others to help.

What Every Caregiver Needs to Know

Dr. Howard Lebowitz, MD

Facilitated by Mrs. Miriam Ribiat

Mrs. Ribiat: What kind of advice can you offer medically and *halachically* to someone who has become the caregiver of an older or ill parent?

Dr. Lebowitz: Let's start by talking about end-of-life-care.

If you are seeking a doctor, you'll find that there are so many medical-referral organizations. It is easy to call and ask for information to make sure that the patient receives the best medical care possible.

Why don't flying referral organizations exist? If you are flying out of the country, don't you want to make sure you fly with the best airline and the best pilot? Even if you are traveling on a short flight, you want to arrive safely. So why are there no organizations to tell you that the best flight to Chicago is JetBlue on Tuesday afternoon, or that you should only take such-and-such airline to Canada? My belief is that the pilot wants to arrive at his destination just as much as you do. A passenger isn't afraid because both pilot and passenger are flying to the same destination.

Dr. Howard Lebowitz, MD, is the founding chief medical officer of AcuteCare Health System's clinical team, which is dedicated to providing long-term intensive care to medically complex patients. He is a graduate of Harvard Medical School and a staff member at Monmouth Medical Center since 2001.

Mrs. Miriam Ribiat is the project manager of Chevrah Lomdei Mishnah. Through her work, Mrs. Ribiat has educated adults and children about aliyas neshamah opportunities and coordinated support services for those who have lost a parent. She is the author of many personal essays on the topics of mourning and loss.

When you are choosing a doctor, it is important to choose one who is on the same flight as you. You want to make sure he is on the same page as you regarding quality-of-life values. As a caregiver, it is important for you to feel comfortable asking the doctor any questions he may have and to really trust him.

Mrs. Ribiat: So you are saying that it is more important to choose a doctor who shares your values and that you feel comfortable with, even if he isn't the most highly recommended?

Dr. Lebowitz: Yes. If that means choosing a doctor who perhaps isn't considered the absolute top, I believe it is a worthwhile trade-off.

It is equally important for the family to choose one member who will act as the liaison between the rest of the family and the doctor. Even more important is for the family to agree on one *rav* who will serve as their *posek* for all issues that might come up regarding the patient's care. When each member turns to his own *rav*, it creates dissension and tension at a time when they really need one another's support. It is also difficult for the doctor when various family members have different ideas and different *pesakim*. And it certainly is uncomfortable for the doctor to be stuck in the middle of that.

Mrs. Ribiat: So what happens if the family isn't cohesive?

Dr. Lebowitz: Generally, I tell them that we do need someone to be the *rosh hamishpachah* (head of the family). I recommend setting up a meeting with the *rav*, the family and the doctor in attendance. This gives everyone the opportunity to air their concerns and opinions and is the most productive way to reach a unanimous decision regarding what is best for the patient.

Mrs. Ribiat: And what happens if the patient chooses a healthcare proxy, and the family isn't happy about it?

Dr. Lebowitz: Most families are healthy enough that it happens naturally. Occasionally there is drama, but I can't say I've seen it happen too many times.

One important subject to discuss with the *rav* and the doctor is aggressiveness of care. The doctor, who understands all the patient's medical issues and all the numbers, can articulate a treatment plan with a tangible goal. The *rav* can then gain a clear understanding and ask the appropriate questions to *pasken* on issues that might come up with end-of-life care.

Our society has created a world in which doctors are painted as evil. Organizations are too often raising the alarm that doctors don't have our best interests in mind, that they are *rotzchim*, that they are dishonest and that you must advocate for yourself and your family. But I don't believe that. Everyone wants to do the right thing. The question is how each person defines "the right thing."

Mrs. Ribiat: But isn't it true that the world feels, *she is 90 years old and not recovering, so why bother treating her?*

Dr. Lebowitz: Our goals and their goals don't coincide.

The world at large emphasizes "quality of life," particularly regarding care of the elderly. I receive calls almost daily from families who are not able to get their older parent into an ICU. The palliative care team think it's a mitzvah to convince family not to pursue care. They aren't evil – they're just misguided.

Mrs. Ribiat: They really think it is right to let someone die, or they just think it doesn't matter?

Dr. Lebowitz: They really think it's right. I don't think anyone stayed up all night studying to become a doctor just to have patients die. How do I know this? Because I am constantly struggling with my own staff of doctors and nurses who don't understand why I am keeping a patient alive. If the person is hardly alive and suffering, they want to know what is the point of all the care we are giving them. But we believe in *Olam Haba*. When medical personnel only see the situation in front of them, of course they wonder why we would prolong the suffering. If it will be today or next week, they say, let it be today. We say, if it will be today or next week, let it be next week. They don't understand that there are eternal benefits to be gained when someone is in this world for even a few more days.

DNR, DNI, DNT (**D**o **N**ot **R**esuscitate, **D**o **N**ot **I**ntubate, **D**o **N**ot **T**reat) all depend on the situation. *Poskim* have very different opinions about resuscitative medical treatment for a patient. It is a mitzvah to try to do everything for the patient's recovery. But I also think it is a mitzvah not to do the few minutes of resuscitative attempts if it is completely futile, just to feel like you are very *frum* and covering all *shittos.*

Mrs. Ribiat: But if it is signed, they don't know if it is futile or not?

Dr. Lebowitz: Right. Also, many *poskim* always say not to sign because they are concerned that the doctor won't try everything possible if a DNR is signed. That is why you need to trust and work with the doctor and the *posek,* whatever the situation might be. I pride myself that I have a lot of patients who never would have been resuscitated in other hospitals but were resuscitated under my care. On the other hand, I also have had many patients that could have had an attempted resuscitation that would have been futile, and I spared them that pain.

Mrs. Ribiat: Resuscitation is painful?

Dr. Lebowitz: It can be. But part of the consideration is that at the time of *yetzi'as haneshamah,* it is so much more meaningful to have the family sitting around saying Tehillim rather than to have the family being kicked out of the room and a bunch of strangers working on the patient. There is a way to live and there is a way to die.

Mrs Ribiat: Thank you for clarifying that. Can we actually define the terms we mentioned earlier?

Dr. Lebowitz: A family needs to discuss the following concepts with their *rav*:

DNR – **D**o **N**ot **R**esuscitate – after a patient already has a cessation of cardio-pulmonary activity and they are dead. One should ask if after the heart has stopped and the patient is not breathing, resuscitation should be attempted.

DNI – **D**o **N**ot **I**ntubate – when the patient has an illness that may lead to a respiratory demise. One should ask if the patient should be allowed to die naturally or be intubated and placed on a ventilator.

Some *poskim* say that regardless of the situation, if the patient will live a few more hours, he should be placed on a ventilator, while some *poskim* rule that if a patient is dying and is in pain and doesn't want to be intubated, it is not necessary to do so.

DNT – **D**o **N**ot **T**reat. I believe this is never *halachically* appropriate. Every patient deserves to receive IV fluid, antibiotics and medication to make them more comfortable.

Mrs. Ribiat: Do families ever ask you if it is time to say *viduy*?

Dr. Lebowitz: Yes, but I try not to mix roles. Let me retain my role as the doctor and let the rabbi guide regarding any *halachic* decisions, especially because each family has its own values in this area, as well as its own *minhagim*. That said, I will call *bikur cholim* or the *chevrah kaddisha* on the family's behalf.

Mrs. Ribiat: Is there anything for a family member to be cognizant of if the patient is awake and aware of what is happening?

Dr. Lebowitz: People should always be very sensitive while near the patient's bedside, regardless of how aware we make think they are. I tell my staff that we have to assume the patient can hear us, and therefore *we should be careful with how we speak. We should certainly never say anything frightening or inappropriate.*

In the same vein, family members should serve as a reassuring presence at the bedside. I have had family members who operated like coaches, i.e., "Come on, Mom, you can do it!" But what the patient really needs is a loving, quiet comforting presence. "I'm here for you, Mom. I love you."

Mrs. Ribiat: Do your patients ever go from under your care in the hospital to hospice?

Dr. Lebowitz: Occasionally. But in most cases they need so much palliative care. Transferring to hospice is so difficult. They are dependent upon too much technology.

Mrs. Ribiat: Do people become upset if you mention hospice?

Dr. Lebowitz: Just today I released a patient into hospice because he wanted to die at home. For my Jewish patients, it is a rarity to want hospice.

Mrs. Ribiat: They don't want to die at home?

Dr. Lebowitz: Again, they are dependent upon so much technological care that it would be too difficult. I am for hospice if there is a place for it. But a lot of hospice companies give the impression that they want the patient to die. As we mentioned before, they feel that if the patient will die tomorrow, then why not die today? I have been in many situations where I had to intervene between families and hospice.

Mrs. Ribiat: So you are like the savior doctor? You really work with patients until the very end?

Dr. Lebowitz: I try my best. As I said, it is a mitzvah to do all that we can.

KEY POINTS:

- It is important to choose a doctor who shares your values regarding end-of-life issues, even if this means bypassing the top medical professional.

- The family should choose one member to act as a liaison between the rest of the family and the doctor, as well as a *rav* who will rule on all issues regarding the patient's care.

- It is valuable to set up a meeting with the family members, the patient's primary physician and the designated *rav* regarding which treatment plan should be pursued.

- Torah Jews are often at odds with the world at large regarding quality of life versus prolonging life. The outside world fails to understand the benefits gained when someone is in this world for even a short time longer.

- DNR (**Do Not Resuscitate**); DNI (**Do Not Intubate**); DNT (**Do Not Treat**) all depend on the situation, which is why it is crucial to work with and trust both the doctor and the designated *posek*.

- Always be sensitive when near a patient's bedside, regardless of how aware the patient seems to be.

Caring For Ill and Aging Parents – Mental Health Challenges

Mr. Abba Cohen, LMHC

T HE TASK OF PROVIDING CARE FOR A PARENT who is terminally ill or whose health is in a state of decline is a challenging and taxing one even under the best of circumstances. When there is a history of emotional-health difficulties, though, this task can be overwhelming to the point of utter exhaustion and with a likelihood that negative feelings such as anger and resentment can come to the fore and pose a serious obstacle to the care that the adult child caregiver is providing. Below we will explore a few of the more common challenges to the caregiver's mental health, as well as offer some suggestions as to how to handle these challenges.

ONE OF THE HARDEST INITIAL CHALLENGES WHEN witnessing a parent's declining health can be the simple acknowledgement that this is in fact the case. We have the tendency to hold on to our perceptions of people and things – and for good reason. Firstly, we want to believe that the world is a consistent and stable place and that the manner in which we know and experience

Challenge: Adapting Perceptions to Reflect Changes in Reality

---

Mr. Abba Cohen, LMHC, appreciates the challenges presented by complex dynamic systems. He has experience working with couples, parents, children and administrations in various settings, such as schools and clinics. He currently maintains a private practice in Brooklyn, Cedarhurst and Queens, where he takes an emotionally-centered, multifaceted approach in his work.

the world and the people close to us today will be the same tomorrow, the following day and for the foreseeable future. While this mindset is helpful in that it allows us to better predict and navigate the world and our relationships, over time, realities can change, and we need to adapt our perceptions accordingly.

Our need to hold on to past realities and mindsets is even stronger when it comes to our perception of our parents. After all, they are the people who raised us and whom we have become accustomed to turning to for support, guidance and advice. They have always been *our* caregivers. Noticing and eventually accepting that these roles might be in the process of shifting and might soon become reversed, and that we as adult children might need to provide ongoing care for them, can be a daunting and frightening thought that we might seek to deny or avoid. When unresolved emotional issues are present, these can exacerbate our difficulty in acknowledging these types of changes; we might invest even more in maintaining and holding onto an old and possibly outdated image and understanding of our parents.

One somewhat obvious way to ensure that we aren't missing out on attending sufficiently to a parent who is need of our care is to pay close attention to the parent's daily routine and functioning and to ask ourselves some basic questions: Has dad been taking care of his basic hygiene? Is mom eating regular meals? Have they had any accidents lately? Are they showing any signs of confusion or disorientation? Though these things might sound obvious, since we're very much used to assuming certain basic skills and patterns that have been in place for decades, we can easily overlook these signs that our parent is in need of our care.

Sometimes even after being confronted with clear signs of a parent's decline in health, one still finds themselves unable to shift their perception and may seek to avoid the topic altogether or to deny this new reality. Anger and resentment can accompany this approach, as it can become very taxing mentally and emotionally to maintain the unrealistic image of one's parent as being self-sufficient and healthy in the face of clear evidence to the contrary. If this approach is maintained, it will unfortunately become debilitating to both caregiver and parent. In such cases, it is highly advisable to seek support from a mental-health professional.

WHEN WE ARE HEAVILY INVOLVED IN CARING FOR OUR parents' needs, we might feel overwhelmed and exasperated at

Challenge: Dealing with Unhealthy Interpersonal Dynamics

times, or we might experience feelings of anger or annoyance. In most cases, this is not necessarily a cause for concern. Providing ongoing, long-term care for our parents is tiring and draining, which alone can provoke negative feelings. We might also feel unduly pressured or overly taxed by their expectations of us as adult children. Those expectations can become unrealistic or simply not feasible given our other commitments, such as work and family. When we are raising younger children in addition to providing care for ailing parents, it can be especially difficult to balance these competing commitments. Even when parents have realistic expectations with regard to the care they receive from us, we still might put unrealistic pressure on ourselves and feel guilty when we can't provide our parents with the time or level of care that we feel we should be providing.

These challenges and periodic negative feelings are typical. Nonetheless, it can be helpful to discuss these issues with a qualified *rav* who can provide guidance with regard to balancing our commitments; these can have *halachic* implications as well. An objective family member or friend can also be indispensable in helping us create a healthy and realistic set of expectations surrounding our care for our parents and helping to assuage typical guilt and negative feelings that we may harbor as a result of trying to maintain untenable expectations of ourselves. In such situations, experiencing periodic negative feelings of mild intensity, which don't interfere with our ability to function, is typical and not a reason to be concerned.

When there's an unhealthy dynamic in which the parent consistently makes unreasonable demands or uses guilt in an ongoing way in order to pressure others to accede to their requests, the caregiver is likely to experience negative feelings, such as anger and resentment, guilty feelings or feelings of being drained and depleted. When a parent is not able to recognize their child as an independent entity who has a basic need and obligation to care for themselves and their immediate family, this is one indication that a dysfunctional dynamic is present.

Even though it is typical to experience negative feelings to some degree in any stressful situation, in an emotionally healthy environment, both parent and child will be able to communicate their needs and feelings in both directions.

In caregiving situations where unhealthy dynamics are present, full awareness of the other person and communication can be one-sided. When there's a lack of awareness of this underlying unfairness and one-sidedness, negative feelings can quickly set in, become somewhat constant and intensifying over time despite one's best efforts to be rid of them. In such circumstances, one should seek support from a mental-health practitioner who is familiar with such dynamics.

Challenge: Dealing with Caregiver Burnout

IT IS VERY EASY TO LOSE SIGHT OF ONE'S SELF AND one's own basic needs when caring for an ailing parent whose needs can feel all-encompassing and overwhelming. There are many reasons why a caregiver is pulled into a caregiving situation that leads to the caregiver becoming neglectful of his/her own basic needs (i.e., proper nutrition, sleep, exercise and rest). "Caregiver burnout" is a very real concern. In fact, studies have shown a highly significant increase in the likelihood of the caregiver experiencing serious, long-term emotional and medical issues when experiencing burnout for any extended length of time. It is critical for the sake of the caregiver, their family and their parent that the caregiver recognizes when they are suffering from burnout and takes the necessary steps to properly care for themselves. As is true in many other helping situations, one truly must first put on their own "oxygen mask" before attempting to put on others' oxygen masks. Some of the ways that healthy caregivers can avoid burnout include the following:

1. **Realizing that it's okay to ask for help.** This does not mean that you are weak, incapable or failing in any regard. It simply means that you, like everyone else on the planet, are human and have basic needs, which sometimes require help and assistance from others in order for you to meet them.

2. **Taking breaks.** By giving yourself intervals of time during which you can focus on yourself, relax, eat or exercise, you are actually also helping your parent by ensuring that the person whom they depend upon (you!) is the healthiest and best caregiver possible. Properly caring for yourself does not mean you are neglecting

your parent. If you neglect your needs, however, you may well ultimately become less capable of being there for your parent.

3. **Finding substitute caregivers.** Even if only for short intervals, it can be an enormous relief to find someone whom you trust to take over for specific lengths of time in order to allow yourself time to care for yourself and/or your immediate family. Again, this is not about you being in any way neglectful in your caregiving duties and responsibilities toward your parent. Quite the opposite. By periodically "handing off" the care of your parent to a trusted friend, relative or professional care-provider, you are maintaining your own health, peace of mind and sanity so that you will be better able to be there for your parent over the long term.

Providing care for our parents as they age or become ill can be a demanding experience fraught with physical, emotional and practical challenges. When we do our best to understand these challenges and look for ways to address and navigate them, while also keeping our own needs in mind, we stand the best chance of being able to manage and provide the care that we aspire to provide and of being there for our parents in the best way possible.

KEY POINTS:

- Acknowledging the reality of a parent's declining health can be one of the most difficult initial challenges a caregiver will face. Unresolved emotional issues can make this even harder.

- It is easy to overlook signs that a parent might require the child's care, since children are used to assuming certain patterns and behaviors are in place.

- If one finds himself feeling resentful and angry at the changes in their parent's reality, it is advisable to seek the support of a mental-health professional.

- Periodic negative feelings, including self-imposed pressure, annoyance, feeling overwhelmed and/or guilt are typical for a caregiver.

- Speaking with a qualified *rav* and/or objective family member or friend can help in setting guidelines to balance commitments and establish realistic expectations as a caregiver.

- In an emotionally healthy situation, the parent and child will be able to communicate their needs and feelings; when there is a lack of awareness of the needs and feelings of the caregiver, this is a sign of an unhealthy dynamic.

- It is critical for the caregiver to take steps to avoid burnout – for the sake of the patient, the caregiver and the caregiver's family. These include asking for assistance; taking breaks; and finding substitute caregivers.

The Challenges of Caregiving

Mrs. Hadassah Goodman, LCSW
& Mrs. Tehila Weisberg, LCSW

CAREGIVING IS A NATURAL ROLE MOST YOUNG adults experience as they build their own families. It is one of the joys of life that certainly presents its own challenges and opportunities for personal growth. We call that type of caregiving "parenting," with clearly defined roles and parameters, with guidelines that are *halachically, hashkafically,* and socially prescribed. This is part of the natural order of life: adults care for their children.

We, as adults, work hard and take pride in the gift of the parenting role. Sometimes, however, the natural order shifts. The **child** needs to become the **caregiver** for the **parent**. This is a most complicated form of caregiving – when aging or illness present a different need and dynamic. Sometimes the natural order for a married couple also dramatically shifts from a mutually shared, cooperative relationship to one in which one **spouse** becomes the **caregiver** for the other **spouse**. This article will focus both on caregiving for a parent and caregiving for a spouse.

The changing needs and realities of the parent or the spouse, now altered by illness or incapacity, as well as the needs of the **caregiver**, are significant and important. However, we focus on the needs of

Mrs. Hadassah Goodman, LCSW, is a licensed clinical social worker and facilitates support groups for women at different stages of life at LCSC, Lakewood, NJ.

Mrs. Tehila Weisberg, LCSW, is a licensed clinical social worker, facilitates several support groups, and offers counseling for caregivers and their families at LCSC, Lakewood, NJ.

LCSC, Lakewood Community Services, Corp., is a family service agency offering support groups, individual and family counseling, and consultation. For more information, call LCSC: 732-886-6964.

the patient because we've accepted fulfilling those needs as our new mission. We are committed to fulfilling that mission to the best of our ability. Each person works "to do it right" for all the unique reasons relevant to their personal situation. Whatever the case may be, there is so much "doing" in the caregiving role, and it is critical to acknowledge that to ourselves and to commend ourselves for all that "doing."

Providing care for someone in need is basic to who we are as Yidden. We are *rachmanim bnei rachmanim*. Sometimes we shorthand the idea and refer to it as, "it's in our DNA." Caregiving also reflects our unique relationship with Hashem as we work hard to emulate His trait of *rachmanus* and *chessed*. We take pride in this, both individually and communally. While it defines who we are, it also defines so much of what we do and how we do it. When the need walks through – or sometimes "crashes through" – our door, our home and our family, it can also bring with it the strong desire to do the right thing – to rise to the occasion; it also brings far more challenges than we might anticipate.

While caregiving can be a challenging and stressful role for an adult child or a spouse to accept, it can also be a very rewarding opportunity in a profoundly meaningful and soul-expanding way. The greatest challenges in life can become special opportunities for true personal growth.

For the parent or spouse who now needs care, whether in their own home or in a different living arrangement, this new stage can involve life-altering changes. Even under the most ideal circumstances, the parent/spouse is making significant adjustments to their new reality. In any number of life's daily functions, the parent/spouse cannot engage in the routines to which they were accustomed.

The parent or spouse is still parent or spouse, even if they are now more in a "patient" position. As the dynamics have shifted – whether they are physical, medical, cognitive, or emotional – and often in combination – new dynamics emerge. This can require sensitivity to the parent/spouse's new reality; arrangements for that person's safe and comfortable living environment; acquisition of new information/knowledge by the caregiver child or spouse; as well as some additional points that will be highlighted below.

WE ALL WANT TO "DO IT RIGHT" – WE WANT TO DO IT right for our parents; at the same time we want to do it right – even as

Doing It Right – Is That Possible? we work to keep our marriages functioning well; we want to do it right for our children – for each child and their specific, individual needs; we even want to do it right for ourselves – yes, there is a self in this picture; we might even want to do it right because, after all, how does it look to others?

We certainly want to do it right for Hashem.

The pressures and increasing expectations for caregivers can be daunting, with myriad stressors, and at each new turn of events, at each escalation of crisis, we are faced again and again with this challenge of "doing it right." Even if the domain of "do it right" might shift slightly, the challenge can be overwhelming and exhausting, both physically and psychologically, possibly with new or added *halachic/hashkafic* dilemmas. There is also a consistent concern about the impact on one's immediate family.

One might think that because we are caring people, and our communities have established excellent organizations that offer direct help and support, the challenges could be managed, as if that support – in deeds, in dollars, in *davening* – would make it all manageable. Unquestionably, this help and support can assist us significantly, but it does not take away the angst and the exhausting pressures we experience within our own family setting as we try so hard to do it right.

CAREGIVING TOUCHES SO MANY ASPECTS OF DAILY life, but the physical and/or immediate medical needs often seem

Physical Care to take priority. Balancing the ongoing care includes a wide array of responsibilities. Some or all of the following may apply:

A. Setting up and maintaining living arrangements, whether in the same house, moving the parent to an adult child's house, or finding and securing another living arrangement

B. Seeing to personal hygiene, bathing and personal care

C. Providing meals and ensuring good nutrition – sometimes new or special diets; maintaining feeding tubes; planning, shopping, cooking, serving, cleaning up

D. Coordinating medical consults and follow-up; getting to and from doctors' appointments and/or treatment protocols

E. Managing medication, which can change often

F. Securing necessary equipment, including special beds, ramps, chairs, and other medical equipment that require set-up and maintenance

G. Implementing some physical activity and exercise

H. Managing finances

I. Supervising and overseeing the hired caretaker

J. Coordinating the daily schedules

Sometimes the need to manage these requirements occurs gradually, allowing some time for adjustment and thoughtful decision making, and sometimes it happens quickly and very unexpectedly. Sometimes the parent/spouse is eager for and comforted with family help; sometimes they are not enthusiastic or comfortable with family help. Sometimes the person is confused about why there is a new arrangement or why the adult child is so involved in what had previously been personal self-management.

Further complications may develop over time, with an escalation of medical needs, which can mean conferring with healthcare providers; making important and sometimes critical life-support decisions; and consulting with a *rav*. At the same time, the business of one's immediate family's needs vies for center position.

Routine is not part of a caregiver's vocabulary. No two days are the same, and no two urgent situations are the same. There may be changes in health needs, in weekday schedules, for Shabbos scheduling, for *yom tov* arrangements, etc. Immediate and extended family plans present their own challenges. Rain, snow, wind, sleet, or heat also shift plans. Caregivers may come to realize they can only count on one constant – change.

ANOTHER IMPORTANT CONSIDERATION IS FULFILLING the patient's social needs, but this may get lost in the urgency of other factors, as medical, physical, and familial needs jostle for attention. However, these social needs – including companionship, regular conversation and retaining social connections – need to be on our priority list. A personal sense of purpose and value are vital for every person, perhaps even more so for someone struggling with physical limitations, medical needs, memory loss, cognitive shifts/losses, and emotional challenges.

Social Needs

Particularly for a person who was active and socially connected, the changes brought on by illness are a serious challenge. It is so important for the patient that the day-to-day connections, activities, business, *davening*, cooking, learning, shopping and general "real living" continue. Filling the day for the patient presents its own unique challenge; keeping those connections active and open can help with healing. And hopefully, this can forestall further decline cognitively, emotionally, physically, and even medically. Thus, trying to find opportunities for connection and social activities and maintaining regular opportunities for social stimulation are of prime importance.

We need to be creative and consider alternative opportunities to keep the person engaged and mentally stimulated, but it can be challenging to do so. Some options that might be helpful to consider include having the parent/spouse join a seniors' group; arranging a schedule of visitors, whether family, neighbors or friends, with whom to exchange conversation or play some games or puzzles; or helping the person work on a simple craft activity. Again, as it can vary according to different needs, other possibilities to stay connected or offer important stimulation could be tuning in to telephone or recorded *shiurim,* listening to audio books or enjoying something musical. Certainly, engaging in basic exercise as part of a strength-building routine can be beneficial for everyone.

Even with several options available, many caregivers find arranging these kinds of activities significantly challenging. There might be issues with hearing, vision, mobility or cognitive limitations that can make it harder for the parent/spouse to engage in some of these valuable activities. There might also be limited services available or limited financial resources. Yet we will work to explore possibilities, come up with ideas, try Plan A and then move to Plan B.

EACH SITUATION BRINGS ITS OWN NEW PLAYBOOK:

Changing Dynamics

How will I, child/spouse, adapt to this? How will I plan and/or manage caring, feeding, lifting, medicating, bathing, dressing/undressing, transporting, communicating, consulting, *davening*? What is my role at this moment? How can I prepare for the shifts in our roles? How will I help occupy my parent/spouse all day? Many factors can affect the ever-changing scenarios.

Even when there is a loving, caring, mutually respectful relationship between parent and adult child, or between spouses, when illness or incapacity strikes, that balance is upset as roles shift and needs change, often drastically.

One woman described her relationship with her now very ill mother: "We had a 'delicious' connection, and now that it is so changed, so hard, and brings so much stress – I worry that I'll forget the good times."

Caregiving can also bring some tough questions to the fore: "If I was not the easiest child – is this my payback?"; "If my sibs and I often bickered as teens – how will we work together to take care of our parent?"; "If I'm the only child in this town, how will we sibs share the responsibilities?"; "If my spouse was usually the person who arranged for daily living matters or balanced the checkbook – how can I do that now?"; "I relied on him/her for so much – I'm so scared now/I feel paralyzed." These are just some of the issues about which caregivers might worry.

The questions and concerns are all real, valid, and can be daunting. These are concerns that many people often struggle with. We may not be aware of this because "we don't talk about these matters publicly." When asked, we say, "*Baruch Hashem,* fine." And, in many ways, we are, "*Baruch Hashem,* fine" and very grateful. But it is not unusual to grapple with internal concerns that can weigh heavily on our minds and need to be processed.

CAREGIVERS CAN EXPERIENCE A BROAD VARIETY OF

Caregivers' Feelings

feelings and many shifts in those feelings, as time and conditions shift. It is so important to identify the feelings; to name the feelings is to respect that they exist. If the feelings exist and can be named, then I, the caregiver, the holder of those feelings, can respect myself and honor myself for what I'm doing – even if the situation is not exactly as I'd like it to be.

We might be feeling overwhelmed (both physically and emotionally), exhausted, hurt, lonely, frightened, disappointed, embarrassed, frustrated, angry or resentful, inadequate, guilty (sometimes *very* guilty!), ashamed, uninformed, tired – very, very tired.

One caregiver poignantly described that she "just felt like mush."

Inherent in many aspects of aging and illness is the natural decline of growing older, made more complicated by illness, especially since illness and its results are unpredictable. While the caregiver might do everything to be supportive and present and might make all the arrangements that are realistically needed, the outcome is not always as we hoped and *davened* for. Caregivers can feel perplexed, frustrated and/or sad: "We did everything we were told to do, everything we thought to do, we followed every protocol and all the advice we were given, so why is my parent/spouse back in the hospital again?"

A caregiver spoke about the depth of her sense of frustration. She spoke about doing so much to make her mother comfortable and to get the right medical help. For about three years, things were okay. It felt so positive to be the caretaker and to see that her mother was comfortable and managing. But then Mom's situation suddenly changed; the caregiver adapted to the changes, but Mom was not improving. In fact, the situation was deteriorating. It felt overwhelming and very frustrating that "we were doing so much – went for medical consults, changed the meds, encouraged the person – we tried again and again, doing all the right things, and the situation was not improving."

Another source of frustration can arise when we see that the parent/spouse we love and want to help is not making wise choices about diet, or therapy, or other prescribed interventions. And when/ if the caregiver is not able to be there for their own family in a way they would have otherwise, frustration about those limitations can also be intense.

Some of these painful feelings can take the caregiver to feelings of guilt, shame and self-questioning. "Why didn't I/we do ...?"; "I should have…"; "If only I/we had done, or said, or remembered, or went, or, or, or."

Regret and remorse are another, similar set of challenges some face. We committed ourselves to "doing it right," and we did everything that was "right" – the changes occurring *now* for the parent/spouse might be part of the natural course of aging and illness. We did all the running and schlepping, all the basics and the extras, and yet we might still feel that it was not enough. There are also those who tend to want to do things "perfectly"; that in itself can sometimes be an admirable trait. But in this new script of life when there are so many variables, getting it "perfect" is often not realistic. Regret and remorse are normal and natural; the challenge is to be careful not to allow those feelings to consume us. While we work hard, so very hard, to do everything that is needed, we want to keep in mind the primary goal: to be there for the person, our parent or our spouse and ensure that their needs are carefully met and addressed. We need to look with positive appreciation at what we have, in fact, accomplished for the patient.

As we reflect on the parent/spouse whom we knew as vibrant, active, able to care for self, to care for others, and/or was productive and respected, we can be overcome with a sense of sadness. Life is so different now than it was. The parent or spouse seems like a completely different person. We can feel profound grief for the loss of the parent/spouse we knew – who is no longer as they were. Sometimes that sadness can bring one to feelings of anger about the current loss, and there may be deep, painful feelings about anticipated loss. These are normal, universal feelings.

As we talk to women and men who are juggling their roles as caregivers, we meet them in small organized caregivers' groups, as well as in informal, neighborhood caregivers' groups, hospital settings and nursing homes. Often caregivers describe their current situation as "my new – very painful – normal."

It can be a hard, slow process to reach the point of saying "this is our new normal." The shift to caregiving is a unique and difficult transition, and acknowledging one's changed reality is an important part of coping. Sometimes a caregiver comes to this realization on their own, and sometimes they seek and find support in caregivers' support groups (either formal or informal), with a professional therapist, or through the attention of ongoing supportive family, a helpful friend, or a *rav*.

We are all familiar with the flight attendants' instructions to first place the oxygen mask on the adult who is caring for the younger passenger. This analogy can apply to successful caregiving, as well.

An important principle in successful caregiving is self-care by and for the caregiver. There is so much "doing" in the caregiving role that is critical to acknowledge that to ourselves and to take care of ourselves. Self-care can take many different forms: taking time off to relax, to read, or to focus on something else that is meaningful; engaging in some simple, regular exercise; journaling; tuning in to oneself to find a simple, uncomplicated personal "booster." By taking care of ourselves and by commending ourselves for all the "doing," we are ensuring that the parent or spouse we are committed to care for will, in fact and in deed, be even more well-cared for.

Cognitive Changes DEALING WITH COGNITIVE CHANGE IS ITS OWN UNIQUE topic that challenges the patient and caregiver, as well as immediate and extended family members. Because this is a significant topic, it can be so helpful to learn more about the dynamics of these unique changes. We will limit our discussion here and only highlight some relevant points.

Even as we struggle to keep the person's dignity intact, the roles of parent/spouse have shifted drastically; they are still who they are, but they are no longer able to be in that role. Yet we continue to provide honor to and for them by working to maintain the public presentation of the parent/spouse afflicted with memory loss or more serious dementia.

A somewhat common phenomenon is the tendency for repetitive questioning, which can become unsettling and hard to redirect. It is also hard to gently and respectfully redirect or guide the parent/ spouse about poor choices in dress, conversation, or other aspects that come up in a public domain. We always hope to work carefully to address the issues with gently chosen, respectful language and sensitivity to the specific situation.

We might also experience a sense of shame related to the parent/ spouse's behaviors as a result of loss of cognitive functions; this is a normal, though painful, phenomenon. We might also become fearful about genetic implications of any illness. Somehow, it seems that physical or medically driven incapacity is less embarrassing and frightening than cognitive losses from dementia.

Sometimes the person afflicted with dementia will speak about "wanting to go home" or the person will even try to leave the house "to go home." Such occurrences are daunting for the family on many levels: they cause frustration because of the inability to communicate, to understand, and to be understood; they can also feel embarrassing; and they can result in safety concerns. Another common situation is when the patient greets others as if it is now Shabbos, or as if Shabbos is coming soon – even days away. It can be helpful to know, and to let others know, that these patterns are normative for this illness. We can try to change the subject, but it might be more comforting to the patient if we simply go along with their thoughts about place and time. Of course, safety is of prime concern, and all efforts should be made to keep the person physically safe.

It is important to keep in mind that some of the symptoms of dementia and its presentation can be baffling and inconsistent. Internal cognitive connections might not function with any observable consistency. This can make it very hard to create and maintain the safe, supportive, respectful, and loving environment we want for our loved one.

Working with Siblings in Care of a Parent

SIBLINGS WORKING TOGETHER TO CARE FOR A PARENT present unique challenges, as along with the situation comes their family history. The idea of shared responsibility in caring for a parent is further complicated when some of the siblings live in locations other than the community in which the parent in need of caregiving lives. Sometimes the realities of each sibling's life situation, or their different styles of working or functioning, or their own life complications – whether they are known or not by the others – present additional challenges.

Siblings can each have different expectations about their roles or the roles of the other siblings, about setting up plans for the parent, or about anything involving parental care. Sometimes there can be differences of opinion among the siblings about the medical diagnoses, the plan of care, or any of the details involved in the parent's well-being. Sometimes expectations are realistic and can bring greater clarity in the planning and the work, and sometimes those expectations can range from somewhat idealistic to completely unrealistic. When siblings living in distant communities want to participate in care and mainly do so via telephone conversations, those interactions can present another type of challenge for the primary caregiver/s. On the other hand, siblings who call regularly and maintain supportive contact, even if they are geographically distant, offer the primary caregiving sibling very meaningful and valuable support.

Often the home the parent is living in or was last living in before hospitalization or other placement becomes the headquarters for that parent's ongoing care. Caregiving is a heavy burden for any one child and even heavier when other sibs have difficulty sharing the responsibility.

Caregiving can raise old sibling-rivalry issues. Old sibling conflicts or "baggage" ideally need to be shed. If one needs to say, "I can't, or "I won't," it is so valuable to express one's concerns or differences of opinion thoughtfully and respectfully. It is also important to think about how to address each sibling's unique personal and familial realities. And sometimes, in the long years that caregiving may require, those realities will change.

Forgiveness is also so important.

It is very lovely, almost ideal, when the caretaking is shared among the siblings; when the caring is jointly agreed upon, planned, and managed; when the responsibilities are divided; and when the decisions come from collaborative planning. Implementing plans to share the work, share the information, share the decision-making, find time to talk as a unit, or possibly offer time off to the primary caregiver can be very beneficial. It can sometimes be helpful for one sibling to take care of finances, another to prepare meals, and yet others to take on the different tasks.

Expectations need to be addressed. Grandchildren, or other relatives in the neighborhood, can be helpful, but they cannot be expected to take on a caretaking role. As much as we might wish for someone else to step in, it can be unrealistic to expect anyone beyond the adult children or spouse to fulfill caregivers' responsibilities.

It can be very enlightening for a sibling group to **jointly** consult with a professional therapist/social worker or a *rav* to help address some of the possible sibling issues, even before they become problems. Someone with experience and someone outside the immediate group can often reframe and help the sib group set priorities and consider their individual roles. Everyone – parent, adult children, and each of their individual families – can benefit from such wise foresight.

The other possible family scenario is that of the adult child who is an only child and now seems tasked with solo caretaking for the parent. The sense of "aloneness" in the responsibility is profound both in the actual caretaking and in the realm of decision making. Even when there is a supportive spouse working along with the sole adult child, the position is a difficult one. That adult child might have grown up alone, but this stage of aloneness may have a more isolating silence to it. Consultation with a *rav* can be very valuable in broadening one's perspective, clearing the air, and benefiting from a learned third-party view.

Reaching Out for Help

ONE ADULT CHILD OBSERVED: "I'M A VERY CAPABLE *person. I always 'can do' in every aspect of our family's life. I was able to juggle so much – the children, my husband's complicated schedule, my work, our social obligations – and get it all done, and done well. I could almost expand the number of hours in a day to do it all. Now, with my mother's illness progressing, the older children are not getting the attention they need, the younger ones are crying out, my work is suffering. I'm feeling so overwhelmed. It's so hard to face the reality that I'm really not managing."*

Reaching out for help is another aspect of life that some of us find very challenging, especially when until now we have seen ourselves as "able to do it all." Both women and men have been trained by society to feel that they can be independent and juggle everything. Now, as a caregiver, we think, "I should still be able to do it all."

Household help is critical to sustaining this important caregiving role. It is important for the parent/spouse who is the patient, it is important for the rest of the immediate family, and it is very important for the primary caregiver. Perhaps if getting household help was prescribed by a medical professional, it would be easier to accept as a necessity!

As the caregiver/family works to sustain the direct, in-home care, one question often raised is the complexity of bringing a non-Jewish hired caretaker/aide into the house. There are some *halachic* guidelines for which one should consult their *rav*, especially regarding Shabbos and *yom tov* and food being brought into the house. While some families have reported that these can be easily and comfortably managed, for others, adjusting to this reality can prove difficult and stressful. There are no simple solutions, but this kind of hired help is so important, as it affords a critical continuity of the necessary care for the patient. [*Ed. Note: See insert attached to this book:* **Welcome to our Jewish Home: The Home Health Aide's Guide to Basic Jewish Laws and Customs.**]

It is vital to allow time for everyone to adjust to this new arrangement. Sometimes starting with part-time help and moving to full time can be helpful, though that too presents its own set of challenges. Both the host family, the caregiver, and the newly hired caretaker need to learn about each other in this new environment. Sometimes it is hard to clarify roles and establish a mutual and clear understanding of the job description and expectations. Most changes are hard for the patient, whether the change is a step forward or a slip back; in this case, the patient is often not happy about the new arrangement and not happy with a stranger in the house, and those feelings can affect the entire family, as well as the newly hired caretaker. It takes time, sometimes a significant amount of time, for each party to adjust to this type of change, even when it is in the patient's and caregiver's best interests.

With the important focus on adjustment and establishing some predictable routines comes the other reality. Hired caretakers need/request their own time off, have their own personal and familial realities, and sometimes have a high turnover rate. Relieving the hired caretaker so that he/she does not become overwhelmed is also important. Time off and replacements can be significant challenges that make the wished-for routine just "wishful thinking."

Generally, people in caregiving positions find it very valuable, affirming, and illuminating to talk to others in similar situations who have had hired help in their homes. The sharing of practical ideas, experiences, and feelings is both informative and affirmative.

WE ACKNOWLEDGE THAT THIS DISCUSSION IS ONLY A brief review of a subject that can cause great concern for the adult child/ren or spouse who is in a caretaking role. Networking and research for more information and resources can be very valuable. As we give time and focus to each of our varied roles and now to this new role of caregiver,

Valuing Your Role

we are affording ourselves the opportunity to more fully develop yet other aspects of our *tafkidim*, our goals, in life.

This *tafkid*, this goal, may be a much more challenging one. We try hard to do our best to fulfill our responsibility to honor our parent, despite the shift in roles. We are clear about our commitment to be a loving spouse and care for the one in a more dependent and less able position. Maintaining our equilibrium in the face of all the unknowns can become a new *tafkid*/goal in itself.

It is so important to make peace with what can be realistically accomplished and where we need to "let go." It is valuable to recognize and respect what we are actually able to do – even if it may only be maintaining *status-quo*. We need to make time to care for our immediate family – and that includes oneself! It is so important to find the time, the space, the focus to "just be"; it's an opportunity to honor who we are and what we are doing.

Our personal growth is a significant factor in this phase of our lives. We are comporting ourselves in the highest level of *rachamim* and *chessed*.

In a more significant way, caregiving can enable us to provide a special someone's *simchas hachayim* in a most unique way. This may not be what we traditionally think of as *simchas hachayim*; yet comfort, care and caring, providing safety and security, all contribute to that person's *simchas hachayim* in their new phase/stage of life.

We have been given this opportunity to care for and ease someone's pain and difficulties. This offers a new dimension in our service of Hashem. It is an opportunity to develop and expand parts of ourselves: our patience, our follow-through, our commitment and our ability to connect with others for help in this new phase.

It's as if Hashem has invited us to do His work – to partner with Him in caring.

KEY POINTS:

- In the natural order of things, parents care for their children. Sometimes this natural order shifts, and it is necessary for us to care for an ill or aging parent or spouse, which is a most complicated form of caregiving.

- There are often life-altering changes involved for a parent or spouse who requires care, as well as for the caregiver.

- Although the dynamics of the relationship shift when caregiving, it is important to remember that the parent or spouse still retains their position as parent or spouse.

- Often there are internal and external pressures to "do it right" – to give the best care possible. Even with assistance and support, this can create much angst for the caregiver.

- Physical care and/or immediate medical needs of the patient include a wide array of responsibilities. Sometimes the need to manage these requirements occurs gradually, and sometimes it can happen quite quickly.

- It is very important to fill the patient's social needs, which will give them a sense of purpose and value, promoting healing and possibly forestalling decline.

- It is not unusual for a caregiver to grapple with personal/ internal fears and concerns that need to be processed. Caregivers can experience a broad array of feelings, and it is important to identify and respect those feelings. Sometimes it can be helpful to seek support from a professional, within a group setting or individually.

- Self-care by the caregiver is crucial to being able to carry on as a caregiver.

- Along with the reality of cognitive changes in the patient comes the challenge of keeping the person's dignity intact.

- It can be difficult to deal respectfully with ramifications of cognitive changes.

- Often, it is most comforting for the caregiver to go along with the patient's confusion concerning time and place. Whatever the case, the patient's safety should always be of paramount concern.

- There can be multiple challenges involved when working with siblings to care for a parent, including differing expectations about roles and establishing care plans for the parent.

- Caregiving is a heavy burden for one child to carry and is made heavier when siblings have difficulty sharing the responsibilities. It can also be complicated by family baggage, such as sibling rivalry, and siblings' varying life circumstances.

- It is very helpful for siblings to jointly consult with a social work professional or a *rav* to address possible issues and to help iron out a workable plan for the parents' care.

- An only child caring for a parent may feel isolated in their efforts and can benefit from consulting with a *rav* for perspective and guidance.

- Reaching out for and accepting help might not feel comfortable, but it is very important to sustaining one's role as a caregiver.

- When hiring a non-Jewish caretaker, it is important to consult a *rav* regarding *halachic* guidelines.

- In any new caretaker arrangement, it's important to give time for adjustment. It can be helpful to phase in a new caretaker slowly and then add more hours as necessary.

- As we develop various roles in our job as caregivers, it's an opportunity to recognize that this is part of fulfilling our *tafkid* (goal) and trying to bring our spouse/parent comfort and security at this new stage in their life.

How Family Caregivers Should Speak So Professionals Will Listen

Henya Storch, MSN, RN

I AM WRITING IN THE MIDST OF THE COVID-19 CRISIS. Covid-19 has brought into heightened focus many issues related to caregiving. Some issues pre-date Covid-19, and some are unprecedented. Self-care is a prime example of a pre-existing issue. As this is being written, family and paid caregivers are risking their lives to care for Covid-19 patients. Now more than ever it is critical that caregivers self-care: get proper nutrition, sleep, and emotional support; take the time to engage in rigorous sanitation protocols (hand washing, social distancing); and make sure they have and are using recommended PPE (personal protective equipment, including gloves, masks, and gowns).

Other issues are unprecedented. Caregiver-professional communication – the issue that is the focus of this article – has been virtually upended during this crisis. The immediacy and intensity of Covid-19 has thrown to the wind established norms and practices, including respectful communication and transparency between treating professionals and patients/caregivers/family members. Given the sheer number of seriously ill patients and the critical value of

Henya Storch, MSN, RN is a registered nurse with a master's degree in nursing. She is CEO of the Storch Agency International, which specializes in healthcare, business and talent coaching, publicity/PR, and communal outreach. Henya lives in Woodmere, New York.

professional time, these age-old practices have been suspended, much to the frustration of all parties.

It is my hope that with G-d's help, the crisis will pass, and we will return to the normative world of patient care.

Introduction

I WRITE FROM THE DUAL PERSPECTIVE OF A REGISTERED nurse with a Master's degree in geriatric psychiatric nursing and many years of experience in the field, and that of a fulltime caregiver to my aging mother. Both nursing and caregiving are holy callings. I've worked as a public-health nurse and nursing supervisor, operating and surgical-room nurse, congregational nurse, manager of a nutritional medicine doctor's office, director of nursing in a nursing home, nursing instructor at a college, and nursing researcher. While raising my children, I spent twenty wonderful years as a summer sleepaway-camp nurse. I was also coordinator of Rofeh International in Boston, one of the first medical referral networks, under the guidance of the Bostoner Rebbe, Rabbi Levi Yitzchok Horowitz, of blessed memory. It was equally my privilege to serve as nursing adviser and professional-care coordinator to many rabbinical families. These experiences heightened my awareness of the importance of the spiritual and *halachic* dimensions of caregiving.

Today I am a healthcare consultant, while serving as my mother's caretaker – a role I cherish and regard as a privilege. In that role, I have come to better appreciate the perspective of family members seeking to navigate an increasingly complex medical system. My goal in writing this article is to enhance communication between family caregivers and professionals so that the interests of the patient are best served.

Roles and Responsibilities

TODAY'S FAMILY CARETAKER MUST INTERACT WITH a wide range of health professionals. In the olden days, the family doctor was available 24/7, made house calls, often cared for multiple family members, and was witness to and aware of the family dynamics. As medicine has become highly specialized, care today is likely to be more fractured and less personal.

Today, there are hundreds of medical services and sub-specialties offered in multiple venues – doctors' offices, clinics, treatment centers, hospitals, nursing and rehab facilities, and group homes. The most basic office visit to a primary-care physician looks very different than it did even twenty years ago. It is common today to be examined by a physician's assistant or nurse practitioner, often without ever seeing the primary doctor. There are dozens of specialized healthcare technicians – sonographers, phlebotomists, and EKG and x-ray technicians – and many allied professionals, including therapists, medical social workers, dieticians, and pharmacists. In the religious community, there is a dazzling array of volunteer organizations functioning in critical roles: medical and mental-health referral agencies, case-management and funding agencies (e.g., Ohel and Chai Lifeline), Hatzolah, *bikur cholims*, medical-equipment lending *gemachs*, and many others.

Before interacting with any medical professional, the family caregiver needs to ask him- or herself the following questions:

What is my role? What is the goal of my communication with the professional? What is the setting in which we are meeting? With whom am I speaking? What am I not seeing? Why should they listen? What is the best way to communicate? What is the best time for this communication? How should I communicate so that my message will be heard? What if I feel the patient is not being treated properly?

Let's explore each question:

WHAT IS MY ROLE? The family caregiver is an intermediary between the patient and the health-care system. If there are multiple caregivers in the family, it is critical that one person be designated as the point person for all communication so as not to overtax already overworked medical staff. As the point person, the caregiver needs to keep all other family members informed and consult with them on key decisions. The caregiver should also oversee home health aides, ensuring that all medical treatments and daily-living recommendations are being adhered to, including medications, food and drink, hygiene, and monitoring of vital signs and weight.

WHAT IS THE GOAL OF MY COMMUNICATION? The goal is to optimize the quality of the patient's treatment and life. Before initiating contact, it is crucial that the caregiver be organized, have all data available, and be prepared to make the conversation short, smart, and pleasant.

An important distinction should be drawn between acute and chronic situations. Acute communications need to be precise and to the point, with the caregiver prepared to present critical patient data (e.g., "My mother had a dizzy spell yesterday morning and again this morning. Her blood pressure was x and her oxygen saturation was y"). Caregivers should prepare and write down questions for discussion of chronic conditions (e.g., "What causes the disease?" "What is the prognosis?" "What are treatment options and risks, including surgery, radiation, medication, possible side effects?" "Are there alternative holistic treatments available?").

WHAT IS THE SETTING? Different settings call for different modes of communication. Acute settings (e.g., emergency rooms, urgent care centers, intensive care units in hospitals) are generally very busy, with staff under pressure. If you have a pressing question, you can attempt to respectfully approach a professional you spot in the hallway. Be aware that they may be involved in caring for other patients and cannot stop to talk to you at that moment. In an in-patient setting, professionals can be paged and will call back as soon as they are available. Especially in acute settings, conversations should be succinct. In long-term or chronic-care situations (e.g., nursing homes, dementia units, psychiatric wards, group homes), you should have the leisure of scheduling appointments or family meetings. A social worker or the head nurse can help make these arrangements.

WITH WHOM AM I SPEAKING? It is vital to understand the scope and limitations of the professional to whom you are speaking. For example, in medical hierarchies, nurses might make room assignments and administer medication, but doctors write admission, discharge, and prescription orders. Whatever their place in the chain of command, it is important to accord *everyone* caring for your loved one (including home-health aides, group home counselors and cleaning staff) the same acknowledgement and respect you would give a physician.

WHAT AM I NOT SEEING? Are you talking to an intern who has gone without sleep for the last thirty-six hours, ministering to deathly ill patients in an intensive care unit? Or perhaps the staff member to whom you are speaking over the phone is facing a backlog of patients standing in front of him or her, waiting to be served?

WHY SHOULD THEY LISTEN? Because it is their job. Nonetheless, it does not give you, the caregiver, the right to threaten or make demands. Instead, appeal to the professional's higher self, and talk in an empathic way ("I see how hard you are working and how many patients you are trying to care for. My mother is in pain. Is there a way perhaps that you could…?"). Recognize that professionals do not answer only to you; they must also answer to their superiors in a complex medical system in which your patient is one of many.

WHAT IS THE BEST WAY TO COMMUNICATE? It is important to weigh the urgency of your communication and, based on that, decide on the most appropriate mode: text, e-mail, fax, telephone call, or in-person conversation. To this we should add telemedicine – a new and very exciting platform that allows one to have a "virtual" meeting with a treating professional. Think carefully when choosing the communication approach: a routine question might not require a phone call. E-mails should include the name of the patient in the subject line and an indication of the time sensitivity and urgency. Do not assume that the recipient of your e-mails or texts knows who you are – make sure to sign off with your name, relationship to the patient, and contact information. Important e-mails and texts should be tagged with receipt confirmations so that you know they have been read. No matter what style of communication you choose, control is virtually always in the domain of the professional, and family caregivers must be prepared to conform to his or her wishes. Adaptability and flexibility are key.

WHAT IS THE BEST TIME FOR THIS COMMUNICATION? Assuming the situation is not urgent, it is best to communicate during normal business hours. This shows respect for the professional.

HOW SHOULD I COMMUNICATE SO THAT MY MESSAGE WILL BE HEARD? Be self-aware, and try your best to control your emotions, tone of voice, and behaviors. Aggressiveness, rudeness, and threatening behaviors are counterproductive and harmful to the patient's well-being. Respect is critical if one wishes to be heard and understood. If the conversation is taking place in the presence of the patient, don't "ghost" or infantilize him or her. Even if the patient suffers from dementia, speaks slowly, is incapacitated, or is hearing or visually impaired, it is important to whatever degree possible not to answer for the patient. Redirect questions from the professional directly to the patient if you can. The caregiver's role is to support the patient and interpret for him or her. Assuming patients can represent themselves independently, it is important to maintain boundaries and promote that independence.

WHAT IF I FEEL THE PATIENT IS NOT BEING TREATED PROPERLY? This is the nightmare of every caregiver. How does one address what one perceives to be poor or inadequate care, and how does one switch physicians or medical settings? Begin by speaking to the assigned professional, who in hospitals today is either the admitting doctor or a hospitalist who is coordinating the patient's care. Patient advocates, social workers, and even hospital chaplains might be able to intervene on a patient's behalf. You might feel uncomfortable seeking a second opinion, but it is common to do so and can even be required by your insurance company in the case of expensive procedures. Community medical referral services (e.g., ECHO) can be very helpful, as can accessing experts in disease-specific Jewish organizations (e.g., BINA for brain injury) or consulting with the patient's rabbi.

Additional Communication Tips:

• Begin by introducing yourself and stating your relationship to the patient. If you are the medical proxy, it is vital that you share this and provide the documentation to back this up for the clinician's records.

• Make sure you give the professional your contact information – cell-phone number, email address, and preferred way of reaching you. If you are expecting a callback from a clinician, keep your phone open and make certain your mailbox is not full. If you will be unavailable or are going on vacation, designate a competent backup and notify all appropriate parties. You will need to orient your substitute so that s/he is very familiar with the patient's paid caregivers, health issues, daily routine, including activities of daily living, doctors, pharmacy, medication regimen, allergies and personal preferences.

• Create a comprehensive typewritten list of patient clinicians (with designations, so it is clear who treats what), medications, and other critical patient information (e.g. allergies) that you can share with alternate family caregivers and that you have ready to share with medical professionals should the patient need hospitalization or emergency care.

- Establish the preferred method of communication for each professional, with minimal background noise distractions.

- Use the professional's name and title – be respectful.

- Do not chew gum, eat, or drink in a clinician's office. If you have a cup of coffee or water, make sure to clean up and dispose of your items.

- During your meeting, do not text or talk to anyone else on the cell phone (unless it is urgent and related to the patient). Remember to put your cell phone on silent mode.

- Do not touch the clinician's papers or other personal objects in the office.

- Never complain to one professional about another (unless you suspect a serious breach of behavior or misjudgment of a situation).

- Ensure the privacy of your patient and others; respect HIPPAA laws.

- Be realistic about the amount of time allotted for a medical appointment; make the most of your session.

- Be presentable – dress modestly, maintain hygiene, be clean and well groomed.

- Be punctual; come early if you need to fill out paperwork.

- Respect the professional's time – avoid no-shows and cancellations. If an emergency occurs and you are unable to keep an appointment, call the office as soon as possible. Briefly explain the situation and apologize.

- Always carry the patient's medication list, insurance cards, photo ID, relevant data (e.g., blood sugar levels, blood pressure readings).

- Be truthful and honest about a patient's history, symptoms, and their compliance with prescribed treatment.

- While building rapport with a medical professional, maintain personal boundaries and limit subject matter to issues regarding the patient.

- Smiles, verbal wit, and humor can be therapeutic. Be careful not to waste a professional's valuable time with inappropriate jokes or lengthy anecdotes.

- Do not pester a professional. Once they have answered your question, move on to the next topic.

- Do not be overly melodramatic – no screaming, sobbing, or yelling. In a life-or-death situation, remain as calm as possible and seek immediate help.

- Don't cut off the professional in mid-thought. It will distract him or her and may be offensive.

- Be mindful of overstepping boundaries and seeking free professional advice in social situations.

- Make sure not to air family discord in front of the professional. Keep all communication targeted to the welfare of the patient.

Strategies to Strengthen Your Relationship with Professionals:

- Jews are called Yehudim because we are *modim* – we give thanks. *Hakaras hatov* – recognizing and acknowledging the good – is a basic Torah value. All verbal and written communication should include "please" and "thank you."

- Show gratitude. Bring boxes of chocolate, fruit, vegetable platters, or plants to the nursing station. Write thank-you notes. Give helpful professionals good reviews. This also makes a *kiddush Hashem*!

- Become friendly with the "gatekeepers" – the secretaries and receptionists who control access to the professionals.

- Think twice before reporting a professional.

- Talk in a way that humanizes the patient and helps the professional empathize with him or her. For example, "If this was your mother or father, what would you do?"

- Stay informed and educated. Seek information channels, such as healthcare conferences and support groups.

- Be open to self-evaluation and helpful feedback. Ask professionals and the patient, "How am I doing?" Hear what they have to say and self-correct if necessary.

Conclusion

CAREGIVING IS A *ZECHUS* (PRIVILEGE) BUT ALSO A demanding responsibility. Self-care is critical. A caregiver must be physically and emotionally healthy so that he or she can provide optimal care to the patient. The caregiver should work daily on his or her *middos* (character traits) – especially patience, humility, and respect for the patient and all caregiving team members.

Patience and Respect for Patients: As hands-on helpers and patient advocates, caregivers are often physical and emotional lifesavers. The Talmud writes that whoever sustains a single soul is credited with sustaining an entire world (*Sanhedrin 37a*). Indeed, every person is a world and deserves respect, without regard to age or health.

Humility: The human condition is fragile, and life is cyclical. The greatest genius can, G-d forbid, in one moment become incoherent and infirm. The strongest person can become paralyzed and totally dependent on others. As we, the caregivers, age, we too may require the care of others.

Patience and Respect for Team Members: The Torah instructs us to always judge others favorably – *b'tzedek tishpot amisechah* (*Vayikra 19:15*). Just as we want others to judge us favorably, so, too, should we show patience and always give professionals and other caregiving team members the benefit of the doubt.

Being aware of these points will help all of us who serve as caregivers to better fulfill our sacred role. G-d is the One who controls the ultimate outcome of all caregiving. By working on our character traits and enhancing our communication skills, we are partnering with the Ultimate Healer in improving the lives of those whose well-being He has placed in our hands.

May we succeed in this holy task.

KEY POINTS:

- Family caretakers today must interact with a wide range of health professionals.

- Know your role: the family caregiver is an intermediary between the patient and healthcare system and is also responsible to oversee any home health-aides. In families with more than one caregiver, it is important to designate one point person to communicate with medical staff and relay information to other family members.

- The goal of communication with medical staff is to optimize the quality of the patient's treatment and life.

- Different settings – acute, in-patient, or long-term care – call for different modes of communication. Does the question require a response immediately or would a scheduled meeting with healthcare professionals be more appropriate? Based on the urgency of your communication, decide on the best way to communicate: text, e-mail, fax, telephone call, or in-person conversation.

- If a situation is not urgent, it is best to communicate during normal business hours.

- Understand the scope and limitations of the professional to whom you are speaking. At the same time, remember to accord the same respect to anyone caring for your loved one.

- Realize that you might not be seeing the whole picture when trying to communicate with medical professionals. They are often dealing with lack of sleep, heavy caseloads, and many other pressing concerns.

- When discussing your loved one, never threaten or make demands; rather, appeal to the professional's higher self and recognize their efforts (i.e., I see you are working very hard… Would it be possible to…).

- If the patient is cognitively aware, one should try to redirect questions from the medical professional to the patient.

- If you feel the patient is not being treated properly, begin by speaking to the admitting physician or hospitalist coordinating the patient's care. If necessary, reach out to patient advocates, hospital chaplains, community resources, or the patient's rabbi to intervene. Consider seeking a second opinion if necessary.

- Recognize the incredible value of what you are doing as caregiver.

- Remember that every person deserves respect, regardless of health or age.

- Realize that someday you too might require the care of others.

- Show patience and give those partnering with you in the care of your loved one the benefit of the doubt.

CHAPTER III

The Inside Story

My Mother and I

Mrs. Chaya Leah Rothstein

MY MOTHER AND I ALWAYS ENJOYED A CLOSE
relationship. My father suffered for many years with a liver disease,

Part I: In the Beginning and after he passed away, I would often speak to my mother four or five times daily. I would check up on how she was doing, and often visit, even if only for a few minutes. She lived a few blocks away, and it wasn't too difficult to swing it.

When my father was gone for about ten years, I began to notice very slight changes in the way my mother expressed herself, or the way she took care of things. My mother was always very fastidious, and her home, her cooking, her presentation, her hygiene, had all always been immaculate. She was getting older. I was her only daughter. I felt it was my responsibility to step in.

The thing that was so incredible was how much support I had from my husband. He always told me that, when it was time, my mother would come to live with us. There was no discussion. That was what we would do. I will always be grateful for his unwavering and straightforward approach: it was the right thing to do, and we would do it.

When my mother started to fail, I had some children who were married or in *yeshivah*. But with six children still living at home, our house was still a bustling household: dinner to serve, laundry to manage, reports to be done, Shabbos and *yom tov* to make – and so much more. And then, there was worrying about my mother.

For a while I had my daughters take turns visiting my mother on their way home from school. It wasn't out of their way. I had three

---

Mrs. Chaya Leah Rothstein considers her main roles to be that of wife, mother and daughter. "Morah Chaya Leah" is the beloved first grade teacher in Bais Yaakov of Detroit, a position she has held for forty years. She is also the author of five children's books. Mrs. Rothstein experienced many challenges as a caregiver while her dear mother resided in the Rothstein home during the last five-and-a-half years of her life. It is her hope that her contribution to this work will serve as an aliyas neshamah for Esther bas HaRav Moshe Chaim HaLevi.

daughters at home, and they each took a turn visiting Bubby. If my mother needed anything, they would try their best to do it for her.

One day my daughter came home and told me how my mother had almost given her credit-card number to a caller on the phone. My daughter had realized what was happening, and she stopped my mother in time. But I knew the time was fast approaching when my mother could no longer be alone.

Another day, another daughter came home and told me, "Bubby's house reeks!" Because she was thirteen-years-old at the time and prone to exaggeration, I figured it couldn't be so bad. I waited until 8:00 PM when things were a little more settled in my house before I went to visit to see what was going on. When I entered the house, the smell was so overpowering that I began to gag. I literally couldn't breathe. My mother calmly told me that she had made chicken soup that day, but after it was made it seemed to her that the chicken must have been spoiled.

I didn't know where to start. The smell was like that of a dead man. It permeated the house, and I needed to vomit – but not now. No, now I had to clean it up and bring in some fresh air to combat the stench. I started opening windows, but it was a November evening, and it was freezing outdoors. My mother started to complain that she was cold, so, of course, I shut the windows.

The kitchen was unbearable. I scoured the stovetop, the pot she had cooked in and the counters. There were still chicken bones – terribly spoiled – in the garbage can. I removed the garbage and scrubbed some more. I went down to the basement to find that the freezer my mother had stored the chicken in, for about a month, was unplugged. I would only learn much later on that sometimes one of the first signs of Alzheimer's disease is a loss of the sense of smell.

When my mother told me that she had actually tasted the broth I almost fainted, but somehow she never got sick from it. Still, it became very obvious that something had to be done.

At about the same time as the soup fiasco, my mother would come to visit our home, and she began to shadow me. I didn't know why she was doing this, and at the time I didn't have a name for it either. Once I started asking questions and learned more about her illness, I would understand that a dementia patient often feels very unsure or afraid. My mother's fears would cause her to follow me wherever I went. There were even a few times that I accidentally stepped on her feet because I didn't know she was only one step behind me! One day she almost followed me into the bathroom, so I had to ask her to wait for me outside.

From the time my father passed away, I would periodically ask my mother whether she would like to move in with us. Her answer was always the same, "Maybe one day, but not yet." Then one Purim she shadowed me for about six hours straight. I turned to her and asked again, "Ma, do you want to come live with us? and she answered, "Yes, I think I will."

Part II: Adjustments

WE HAD MADE THE DECISION TO HAVE MY MOTHER move into our home. Preparing our home for her arrival was a gargantuan task.

We had to sell my mother's home, clean it and pack her up, sell or dispose of those things we couldn't take, and move her by the time the buyers of her house wanted to move in. This was complicated by the fact that I have a summer job out of town, so I had that deadline as well. Add to the equation that my teaching job was to end on the same day that we had to leave town, and you get the picture.

For months on end I went through the home in which my parents had lived for the last thirty-five years. My mother had always kept everything neat, but there was *a lot* of everything – my father's glass collection and my mother's linens, etc. Not only did they have to be dealt with, but they brought back so many memories. Going through all the pictures was almost impossible.

Setting aside a specific time each week for the task was helpful. Each Sunday morning I tackled another part of the house. I included my mother as much as possible. It was so much easier for me when she was a little more clear-minded and able to help me make decisions.

We had decided to make my mother a small apartment within our home. I know that I could have set aside just one room, but I felt that my mother would need quiet, and she would need to have a place to sit and relax, not just to sleep. We renovated three bedrooms, and it truly was a private, peaceful area.

I tried to decorate the rooms to look as much like my parents' home as possible. I was able to find the same exact linoleum for her kitchen area as she had had in her house. Her bedroom carpet was the same color as her original bedroom carpet. I hung her favorite pictures immediately to make the new apartment look like home. Dementia patients are particularly sensitive to unfamiliar environments, but my mother's new living quarters looked familiar, and I think that did help her to better adjust to her new surroundings.

I took my mother along with me as we picked out some new furniture and the colors for her kitchenette. There were times when she didn't remember that we had purchased anything, but it was the best I could do. At least, I reasoned, she did like those purchases when we chose them.

When my mother first moved in, she ate all of her meals with us. As she declined, mealtimes became more and more of a challenge. She would often become very agitated at the table. Once, when one of my children placed his hand on the napkin holder, she started screaming. It became more of a challenge for her to follow conversations. For example, if someone mentioned the weather, followed by someone else piping up about how much homework she had for that evening and another child mentioned that a friend would be coming over, my mother would comment that yes, the weather was very nice. The many conversations were just too much for her, and mealtimes became less inviting and sometimes filled with tension.

I was attending a support group at that time, and I brought up my issue with mealtime. The others at the meeting asked me if I thought my mother could handle multiple conversations at one time. Of course, she couldn't. Then they challenged me as to why I was having my mother eat with the family when she clearly would be more comfortable eating in her quiet room by herself. I was almost angry. I told them, quite self-righteously, that I hadn't brought my mother into my home so that she should be by herself! I wanted her to feel that she was part of my family. *Ah*, they countered, *she feels the love of your family, she just isn't able to sit at the table with them anymore. It's too great of a challenge for her now.* I knew they were right, I was just too sad to admit the truth.

After that revelation, my mother ate in her room. It was quiet, and she was relaxed and happy. It took me a much longer time to adjust. The adjustment to having her live in our home was mine as well as hers, but her needs were the ones we had to honor.

Greater adjustments were yet to come. My husband brought me seven books from the library addressing caring for patients with

Alzheimer's and dementia disease. I read each one thoroughly until I reached the chapter on incontinence. Then I closed it, and went on to read the next book. I knew that I couldn't face incontinence. No way. Not that. Anything but that.

Of course, I was wrong.

When we are caring for someone, we do what needs to be done, whatever that may be.

There was one Shabbos I will never forget. My daughter was engaged to a terrific guy, and he had come to visit for Shabbos. We were having a lovely time, trying to make our best impression on him, when suddenly my services were needed. I closed the doors to my mother's rooms and began the clean-up. I was so upset by the turn of events that I could have cried. Maybe I did. I had a huge job ahead of me, and no one to whom I could voice my frustration. Only gentle words and encouragement were allowed when speaking to my mother. Restraint, restraint, restraint – all the restraint in the world is what I needed.

And it was with restraint that once again I honored my mother's needs. But it was not easy – and to be honest, that was the end of my lovely Shabbos.

KEY POINTS:

- When moving your parent(s) to a new environment, try to break up the cleaning and packing and do as much as possible in advance. This will greatly reduce the stress involved in the move itself.

- Decorating the new environment with familiar colors and objects can make a new place feel like home. This is particularly important in helping dementia patients adjust more easily.

- Anticipating the needs your loved one(s) may have – even in the not-so-near future – should be taken into consideration when setting up a new living space.

- Be open to the idea that situations and needs will change. Flexibility is key.

- Ask your *rav* as questions arise. When situations change, ask again.
- Know that there will be hard days, and easier days. Stating your needs is so important. Stating them calmly is altruistic.

What It's Really Like: Glimpses of My Life as a Caregiver

Mrs. Chaya Leah Rothstein

Explanations

AFTER MY MOTHER HAD LEFT THE HOUSE ON HER OWN, we didn't feel that we could leave her alone any longer. We hired a caretaker to stay with her while I went to work. But how was I to explain this to my mother? She was still able to do so much and to understand so much. And she didn't think she needed anyone to watch her. In fact, she was sure that she didn't need anyone.

When the day came that I told her a woman would be coming the next morning to be with her and keep her company during the morning hours, she asked me, "Why?"

I stood rooted to my spot. I thought, "Hashem, please put the right words in my mouth. How can I explain that we're afraid to leave her alone? I don't want to hurt her feelings, but what can I say?" I must have stood there for a moment or two trying to think of the right words and coming up blank.

Just then my husband came into the room. My mother repeated her question: "Can you tell me why I need someone to be here in the morning? Why can't I be by myself?"

My husband answered, "It's good, Ma, it's good."

"Oh," she answered. And that was that.

Mama

WHEN MY MOTHER NO LONGER HAD THE ABILITY TO make responsible choices, I began to lay her clothes out for the next day. I was so nervous about each thing that I did for her when it was something that most people do for themselves. I was worried about her knowing that she couldn't do it herself and afraid that she would feel demeaned.

As time went on she became weaker and less able to care for herself. Before bedtime, I would take care of her, wash her, help her brush her teeth and help her into her night clothes. It was a tremendous switch. Now I was taking care of her.

I never knew how aware she was that I was now her caregiver. I never knew if she felt bad about the altered reality; it was torture not to know. I had taken parenting classes and heard many *shiurim* about *kibbud av v'eim*, but to this day I have never heard an explanation of how to take care of a parent as one cares for a child and still exhibit the honor one gives a parent.

One Friday night, as I was helping her out of her clothes, she gave a deep sigh. It was unlike her, and I asked her if something was wrong. She looked at me and said, "It's so hard..."

"What's hard, Ma?" I asked.

"It's so hard for you to take care of me."

It was the only time that my mother seemed to be aware that she needed my help. It was the only time she ever expressed it.

"Ma," I said, "That's what I'm here for. Whatever you need, I'm here for you. Nothing is hard. I'm your daughter, I'm here for you."

That seemed to calm her.

I tucked her into bed and she said *Shema*. Then she said to me, "Goodnight, Mama."

AS MY MOTHER'S CONDITION PROGRESSED, SHE ALSO developed a high sugar count. The doctor ordered medication, but now it was important to monitor her sugar count

Would You Like a Chip? daily. I was glad to have a caretaker for many reasons, but especially glad that she was there for the poke each day, as this would have been *halachically* very questionable for me to do on my own parent. My husband would not have been helpful here, as he is squeamish at the sight of blood.

One day my mother's caretaker came to tell me that my mother's sugar level had dropped to an almost dangerous level. Untreated, this could lead to a diabetic coma, or worse. It was important that my mother eat, and get extra sugar very soon, or there could be dire consequences.

I quickly went to my mother and offered her a drink of orange juice, which usually serves as a great sugar booster, but she wouldn't drink. I tried to tell her that it was important for her, but she would have none of it. She didn't want juice, and she wouldn't have any, she explained. *Oy.*

Okay, so she didn't want juice, but her favorite snack was licorice! Great. I ran and got some licorice. "How about some licorice, Ma? You love it!"

"I told you I don't want any, and I'm not going to eat it!" she told me emphatically, "You can't make me eat it!"

Oy.

I don't know if it was the low blood sugar or her general condition that made her unreasonable, but whatever it was, she had to eat. And she had to eat now.

I continued to offer her loads of foods. She refused them all. She wasn't going to eat, and that was final. I didn't know what to do. Then I had an idea.

My mother always liked potato chips but didn't eat them often because of the fat content. To her they were a major treat. But right now, she was belligerent, so I tried a different tactic.

I went into the kitchen and poured a whole package of chips into a bowl. I asked my husband to join me, and we went into her room. I sat down on the couch and started eating chips. I made a big show of each chip that I ate, crunching loudly and declaring that they were delicious! Then I exaggeratedly offered some to my husband, who said, "Oh, yes, I would *love* some chips," and he too began crunching loudly and saying how they great they were. I then offered some to the caretaker, Tina, who was not sure what I was doing. She started to decline, but when I gave her a look, she changed her mind and decided that, yes, some chips would be wonderful.

The whole time I was sitting next to my mother. She watched quietly, almost sulking, until she said, "Aren't you going to offer me some?"

"Oh, Ma, would you like some chips?" I asked.

"Yes, I think I would."

(The upcoming story took place much later in the course of my mother's illness.)

IT WAS EREV PESACH. I WAS EXHAUSTED. I WAS TEACHING and housecleaning and trying to keep life together. But I was almost **Chrein** there. The house was clean for Pesach, and the kitchen was ready. My mother had always told me that the cooking for Pesach was the easy part. Once everything was "turned over" and *Pesachdik*, the cooking was a cinch.

The first thing I prepared each year was the *chrein*. It was the job I liked least, so I wanted to get it done first. The previous year, my mother was still able to speak, and I remembered having brought her into the kitchen to help me make the *chrein*. My mother's *chrein* was legendary. Many a grown man had been reduced to tears, thinking he could handle a generous helping of said *chrein* on his gefilte fish, only to be reduced to intense coughing – and wishing he hadn't been so brave.

I also remembered that I had definitely written down the recipe. I knew the year before that my mother was failing, and I wanted that recipe for all time. I checked all of my recipe cards and couldn't find it anywhere. I checked again and again; it was so frustrating. I just wanted to get my cooking started, and I wanted to make that *chrein*. The problem was, my mother no longer spoke to anyone very much anymore, and I had no one else to ask.

I guess I was very tired or rundown – maybe both. But somehow that recipe started to mean everything to me. I needed it, and I couldn't proceed without it. I wanted to make my mother's *chrein* – I needed to.

I don't know what made me try, but I did. I went into my mother's room and knelt by her side.

"Ma," I said, "I'm starting to cook for Pesach, and I need you to help me make the *chrein*."

She stared straight ahead and didn't move. It was as if I wasn't there.

"Ma," I tried again. "Please, could you help me with the *chrein*? I don't know how to do it myself."

Again, she just stared. I began to cry. I didn't want to, but the tears came on their own. They filled my eyes and slowly coursed down my cheeks. I wanted her back so badly. I wanted to have her help me like she always had. I didn't want to be in charge. I was fifty years old, and I wanted my mother.

Now, I begged. "Mommy, please, I don't know how to make the *chrein*. Could you please help me?" The tears continued. Then, I had an idea. I started the recipe for her.

"Okay, so I'm going to take the *chrein*, and peel it, right?" That was all I said when my mother slowly turned her head toward me. It was my dream come true. She lifted her hands and held one hand out flat. She took her other hand and make a chopping motion. Then she spoke. She spoke!

"You chop up the pieces," she started. I took up where she left off.

"Right," I said, "and then I have to put it in the blender. But what is the liquid that I put into the blender?"

"Half water, half vinegar," she responded.

I knew the rest. The tears were flowing freely down my face. I couldn't stop crying. I kissed my mother on the cheek and thanked her over and over again. I felt that Hashem had blessed me with one more conversation with her.

I returned to the kitchen. I went over to my recipe box to write down the instructions, and there was the recipe from the year before.

The Five-Minute Rule

Mrs. Chaya Leah Rothstein

CERTAINLY I DO NOT STAND ALONE. MANY people have shared equally challenging situations, some with many more obstacles than I.

I have a friend who took both of her parents into her home. Her children were very young, and her parents needed almost constant care. One of her parents needed extensive care in a hospital setting and required transportation back and forth to the facility almost daily. The other parent had suffered most of his life with debilitating disease. It made my situation look like a picnic.

My friend came to PTA conferences one evening. I was teaching her young daughter that year. I asked how things were going. She looked like she was about to cry.

That look was all I needed. I tried to give her encouragement and to remind her what a marvelous *chinuch* it was for her children to witness firsthand how she cared for her parents. Her forbearance was remarkable; her husband, an absolute *tzaddik*, for the entire community could observe how he watched over his father-in-law. In all, they were doing fine.

Now the tears were spilling down her cheeks. Clearly, I needed to stop talking and listen.

She had a hopeless look as she began to explain. She had just had conversations with her other children's teachers. Every single one had told her that she was ruining her children's lives by having her parents in her home. She wasn't paying enough attention to her children, she didn't have enough time for them, they were being neglected... *Oy!* Now here I was telling her that what she was doing was the best thing for her children. She wanted so badly to do the right thing, and she also wanted to care for her parents. She wanted to soldier on, but what of the other opinions? Did they have merit?

She continued to say that so many days were so difficult. She was often stretched in six directions at once. She knew that she was burning the candle on both ends. Her parents needed her, but so did her children. She was so tired and so torn. She needed direction, and I didn't know if I could guide her.

We all have those moments. In the past if something was too tough to figure out on my own, I always knew what to do. Call and ask a *shailah*! Easy enough. Once I ask, I can be confident in my decision, knowing that I've asked *da'as Torah*. What could be better?

But I found that when it came to caring for my mother, I could ask and not necessarily get a clear answer.

Once I asked a *rav* the following question: The doctor had told me that it was healthy for my mother to move as much as possible so that her muscles wouldn't atrophy. So, of course, I encouraged my mother to move and be as independent as possible. However, as her disease progressed, it became increasingly difficult for her to move. Indeed, it became a struggle. So I asked if I should step in and do things for my mother when I see her struggling, or if I should let her struggle so that she would be forced to use her muscles? (To be honest, it was torturous for me to watch her struggling.)

The *rav* answered that whatever I did would be fine. Whichever way I felt I should proceed at any given time would be the right thing to do. I was lost. I needed direction, I craved direction, but I had to direct myself. I prayed to Hashem, and I stepped in to do things for my mother because I simply couldn't watch.

So how to direct my friend now? Certainly I am not a *rav*. I encouraged her to ask, but in my heart I imagined that no one would tell her. But I did add that it had to be good for her children to watch *kibbud av v'eim* in its most beautiful form – that nothing bad could come from doing a precious mitzvah. And one more thing: I had a five-minute rule.

Whenever I had reached the absolute end of my rope, whenever I thought that I couldn't take one more moment of stress, when I was ready to cry at the unfairness of it all, when I felt that I would simply lose my mind, I would ask myself if I could do this for just five more minutes. Five minutes? *Okay*, I would answer myself, *five minutes, but not a second longer*. I would go on. I would remain calm. I could endure just five more minutes. Oftentimes, when five minutes were over, things were a little better. I would take a deep breath and know that I had passed the test of the day. Sometimes things were no better at all, and then I would ask myself again, *can I hold out for just five more minutes?*

I told all this to my friend. She smiled and said that, yes, she thought she could survive for five more minutes.

Years later, she told me that the five-minute rule had saved her. I know it's true because it saved me, too.

KEY POINTS:

- Try to keep an open dialogue going with family members. When we added on to our home, we made sure to give the children plenty of private space, but there were still many adjustments they needed to make. Keep talking, keep asking, and take everyone's opinions seriously.

- Many people will offer advice. Learn to smile and respond with something like, "I appreciate your concern, and I will certainly keep that in mind." Only give it real weight if you feel it's valid.

- Find counsel. It may be your spouse, your *rav*, or your neighbor. Find someone who, in your opinion, is level-headed and compassionate about your situation. Benefit from their wisdom. It will help to dispel doubts and ease your mind.

- Be nice to yourself. You're experiencing a very trying time. Encourage yourself, and treat yourself when you can. Be understanding as you would of a good friend. Hashem knows how hard you are trying, and if He appreciates you, you should appreciate yourself.

Caring For My Father

Rabbi Moshe Haikins

A S AN ONLY SON AND THE ONLY CHILD LIVING in America, I took the responsibility of caring for my father very seriously. The sicker he became, the more he needed me, and I really tried to be there for him. B"H, my wife was very supportive. Not only did she not take issue with my complete devotion, which literally tied me up for entire days, she stood by my side, helping out wherever she was needed.

SEVERAL YEARS BEFORE HIS PASSING, MY FATHER BEGAN displaying symptoms of Alzheimer's. His situation became further complicated when we discovered that he was suffering from colon cancer. I was constantly busy with aides, home-care nurses, rehabs, hospitals and doctors. And each time my father needed to be admitted somewhere, I invested a great deal of time researching the options to make sure he would be receiving the best possible care.

Taking the Necessary Steps

Unquestionably, I was managing a heavy load, but I am grateful that my father had signed a healthcare proxy, putting me legally in charge of his care. Each family has its own dynamics, and even a family in which the members are supportive and loving can have disagreements when caring for an ill family member, causing friction and impeding the family's ability to focus on the patient's needs. In my case, there was step-family involved, which made the dynamics even more complicated. Thankfully, my father had signed papers that prevented many opportunities for dissention, even when there was contention. I always made sure to carry numerous copies of the legal

Rabbi Moshe Haikins is the founder and president of Chevrah Lomdei Mishnah, a non-profit organization that provides the zechus of Torah learning and tefillah l'iluy neshamos, as well as many materials and services for those who have lost a loved one.

paperwork to present to the appropriate authorities in the different facilities to make sure that everyone knew who was the caregiver.

Something else I did that was very helpful was speaking with a *posek* who is knowledgeable in life-and-death issues to discuss the factors I needed to know should it become necessary to make certain medical decisions. He gave me basic guidelines for when to ask a *shailah,* and he gave me his personal cell phone number.

Active Participation

IN MAY OF 2016, MY FATHER WENT FOR ROUTINE bloodwork prior to scheduling cataract surgery. We were frightened to learn that his hemoglobin level was at six, which was dangerously low (the normal hemoglobin level for a man ranges from 11 to 14). It was Friday morning when my father was taken to the hospital. I dropped what I was doing and drove two hours to make sure to be with him, bringing basic Shabbos necessities, as I was unsure if I would be there for Shabbos. The doctors decided that he needed a double transfusion and that he would be released following that, so I decided it made sense for me to return home for Shabbos. As I was driving home, I heard that my father would not, in fact, be discharged before Shabbos. Upon further testing, it seemed that he might have suffered a small stroke. At that point it was too late for me to turn around. But as soon as Shabbos was over, I drove right back.

And so began the journey of caring for my ailing father. After a weeklong stay at the hospital in New York, he was transferred to Leisure Chateau, a rehabilitation center in my hometown of Lakewood. Although we had an aide staying with him, I made sure to visit twice a day, once in the morning and once in the early evening. Besides seeing my father in the morning to say hello and to see how he was doing (if he was awake), an important part of the morning visits was collecting any new medical information from the nursing staff. Additionally, I realized how important it was for the staff members – and this is true in any facility, whether a nursing facility, a hospital or a rehab center – to be cognizant that there were concerned family members who were active participants in the care of their loved one.

I often brought my children with me for the evening visit. At first it was very exciting for the children to come see Zaidy every day. Eventually the excitement wore off for the older ones, but the younger ones liked to come and schmooze or play a game of checkers with him. They always had what to talk about. They were able to repeat the same stories over and over again without their Zaidy remembering that he had just heard the same thing.

My father was in Leisure Chateau for three months, and for those three months, my wife cooked and packed up Shabbos meals, and we and our children stayed in a *bikur cholim* apartment or some other local location so we could spend Shabbos with my father.

Another important thing I was told to do early on was to spend time taking notes about all of the medical issues affecting my father. Doctors and nurses are human and are often overworked. The caregiver has the responsibility to have all pertinent medical information at his fingertips at all times.

During my father's stay at Leisure Chateau, there was constant bloodwork being done, as well as other testing, as they were aware that my father had a hemoglobin issue. Initially, my father was sent a few times to a local hospital for an intravenous dose of venifor, which is supposed to help the body produce more hemoglobin on its own. Each procedure took at least an hour or two, besides the time it took to prepare and transport my father to the hospital. When the numbers were still dropping, he was scheduled a few times for blood transfusions – sometimes a single transfusion and sometimes a double.

However, it became clear to the doctor in charge of my father's care that the fact that the numbers were constantly falling was probably indicative of a greater issue. He therefore decided to schedule my father for a colonoscopy, and we discovered that he had colon cancer. At the same time, my father began bleeding, and the doctor said that we needed to admit him to a hospital immediately. He assured us that the doctors at a nearby hospital could be trusted with my father's care, even if he would need imminent surgery to remove the mass.

Emergency Transfer

ONCE MY FATHER WAS IN THE HOSPITAL, I SPENT TIME talking with an internationally known referral agency, asking the rabbi in charge about securing the best surgeon and care for my father's situation. The rabbi was emphatic that New York doctors are by far superior, and it was worthwhile to transfer my father to a New York hospital, where he would arrange for him to have surgery with a top-tier surgeon.

Without getting into the technical issues, it is no simple task for a layman to secure a hospital transfer once a patient has already been admitted and to get a superior surgeon to take a patient he has never met. This was further complicated by the fact that my father was admitted to the first hospital on a Thursday afternoon, and many of the conversations with the rabbi took place on Friday afternoon.

However, the rabbi did not relent. He insisted on transferring my father. NOW. Not after Shabbos. NOW. He was instrumental in getting an ambulance to do the transfer, and, with the *pesak* of a prominent Lakewood *posek*, both my wife and I (besides my father and the aide), went to New York that Friday night in the ambulance (after having a quick Shabbos meal with the food supplied by the local *bikur cholim*).

Just to put all this in perspective, I was not prepared for this emergency transfer, so it was that I found myself on the way to New York, hot and sweaty, and in my weekday clothes. Add to this the fact that we had two cars at the local hospital – mine and my wife's. My wife hid the keys in a predetermined place, and my two older sons came to pick up both cars after Shabbos. We did have my wallet with us, which we had the aide take into the New York hospital, and when Shabbos was over (quite late, as this was the summer), my wife and I took a taxi to Port Authority and then took a bus back to Lakewood. I only said *havdalah* at 12:30 AM. At 7 AM the following morning, I left again so that I could meet the doctors in New York when they would be doing their morning rounds!

ONE ISSUE WE STRUGGLED WITH WAS THAT MY FATHER was very underweight. Persuading him to eat was very challenging, and

Basic Care – and Beyond

we tried to take advantage of every opportunity to get him to eat. Those of us dealing with aides know that some are good and some are simply not. At one point my father was living in my house. Each morning we tried to make him an omelet, adding a lot of oil and cheese so that it would be as fatty as possible. One morning, the aide piped up, "You know, this isn't good for his cholesterol." The bad news was that my father was sitting right there. I had to pull the aide to the side to tell her that we were following the doctor's orders and that right now, weight gain was more important than worrying about cholesterol. We needed to carefully monitor his weight. Initially we took him once a week, and later twice a week, to a weigh-in station in a local ShopRite where he was able to sit as he was weighed.

Aside from handling my father's basic care and all the day-to-day issues, there were constantly extra things that required attention. During this period, my father underwent cataract surgery; he was also under the care of a podiatrist, a dermatologist, a doctor to check his muscle movements, as well as nurses who came to my house to help him exercise. This was besides the regular doctors' visits and the two separate oncologists that we went to for opinions on how to treat his cancer. But however hectic life became, I knew that I would do whatever I could to help my father.

A few days after Purim, my father simply did not look right. We thought that maybe he had had a stroke. He was scheduled for a double blood transfusion that day, and while he was in the hospital for the transfusion, I called the doctor to squeeze him in for an appointment ASAP. The stroke was ruled out, but the doctor was concerned that my father did not look well, and told us to take him to the ER right away. We took him to the hospital where the oncologist was on staff – close to an hour's drive from our home – rather than to any local hospital, as we felt that he would get superior care there. My wife and I took turns staying there with my father, hardly ever leaving him alone, even though he had a full-time aide.

I made it my business to be there when the doctors were doing their morning rounds and brought a recording device with me. Besides the fact that other family members wanted to hear what the doctors said, it is good for doctors to see that they are being recorded. It definitely motivates them to be more careful with what they say and do with your loved one.

Eventually, my father needed to be intubated, as per the *pesak* that I received from Rav Shmuel Kamenetsky. (I knew to ask this *shailah* based on the information given to me by the other *posek*.) I was unaware that this would be the case, but before he was intubated was really the last time that I had a conversation with my father. Once the breathing tube was inserted, he could not talk, and writing was already difficult for him.

WHEN I ASKED FOR A FEEDING TUBE TO BE SURGICALLY inserted, the doctors didn't want to bother with it. Their reasoning

My Father's Advocate was that it is a difficult procedure, and my father was dying anyway. They did not come straight out to say that clearly, but I had learned how to read between the lines. I knew that it was **not** a difficult procedure at all. What I learned then was that it was very important not to lose my voice as the patient's advocate, that it is okay to ask the doctors questions and that it was my responsibility to insist that all care was up to par.

At that point, since the hospital was no longer helping my father in any practical way, I tried to have my father transferred to LTACH, under the care of Dr. Howard Lebowitz. There, he did receive a feeding tube, as Dr. Lebowitz understood the need. Unfortunately, however, it had to be removed after a short time due to medical complications.

And indeed, dealing with an older sick parent can be fraught with complications. I never knew when there was going to be a crisis. My life was on hold for that last year, as I prioritized my father's care. I made sure that either my wife or I would be in the hospital each morning before rounds began. I kept my recorder with me, and the doctors knew that we could easily replay every word they said.

YES, THE LOGISTICS WERE DIFFICULT. BUT THE HARDEST thing for me was the way my father's personality changed. He was

Incomparable Benefits no longer the father I had known and loved for many years. Odd as it may sound, at times I felt angry at him for it. Of course, I knew the anger was irrational, and eventually it passed.

Looking back today, I realize how much my family and I gained from that hectic, sometimes overwhelming, period of time. My children saw what real *kibbud av* means. And even more than seeing it, they participated in it. For a time, Zaidy was living in my house and then down the block from me. When he was down the block, every night, a different daughter took a turn sleeping in his apartment. My oldest daughter would literally sit and feed him. There were so many visits and conversations with Zaidy. My family gained immeasurably by having him so close for all that time.

Something else should be mentioned here: taking care of one's parents is not just a nice thing to do – it's mitzvah, which means it's something you are **obligated** to do. (And you never know; maybe your children will in turn take care of you in that fashion if that time ever comes…)

Rabbi Avigdor Miller *zt"l* talks about family sometimes feeling relief after a loved one passes on after suffering for a long time. Perhaps on a subconscious level I have felt that relief. But there is no guilt. I did all that I could do for my father. And he gave my family a tremendous opportunity that not every family is *zocheh* to have. It is my hope that anything gained from this article should be for an *aliyas neshamah* for Avrohom Yitzchok *ben* Chayim Tz'vi, *a"h.*

KEY POINTS:

- Taking care of a parent is a HUGE responsibility. You will be making life-altering decisions.

- Taking care of a parent is a HUGE *zechus*. Giving back to your parent in some miniscule way is only a fraction of the *hakaras hatov* that you owe your parent.

- Make sure your parents have signed healthcare proxy documentation and that you have numerous copies of it available with ease.

- Establish a *rav* with appropriate experience who can give you awareness of potential *shailos* and who can guide you through medical decisions.

- Visiting your loved one's nursing facility/hospital/rehab center often is crucial.

- Take notes on what the doctors and nurses tell you, as well as what you see.

- Record doctors if possible.

- Be aware that feelings of frustration and possible anger at the loved one you are caring for are NORMAL.

- Involving your children in the care of your parent is a lesson in *kibbud av v'eim* that cannot be replicated anywhere else.

- Involving your children in the care of your parent is a priceless opportunity for quality family time, with face-to-face contact and with expressions of love that cannot be duplicated elsewhere.

Perspectives of a Daughter

Mrs. Miriam Goldberg

THERE IS NO EXPERIENCE LIKE LIFE EXPERIENCE, and as I had the privilege – and the challenge – of caring for my mother during the years and months prior to her passing, I feel that perhaps others can gain something from what I learned during that time.

Several years before her *petirah,* my mother and stepfather moved into a ranch house two houses away from my family's home. I must concede that the logistics could be complicated, but the close proximity allowed me to manage both their home and mine; as my mother's dementia progressed, the responsibilities increased.

I would be remiss if I did not mention how despite my mother's increasing limitations, my stepfather continued to treat her with respect and love. In the initial stages of her dementia, he would compensate for her shortcomings, and I remained blissfully unaware of how deep those shortcomings were. He took on more shopping, as well as light cooking – not easy for someone his age with his own health issues. There were times when he would shrug his shoulders and say to himself, "If she could she would, but she can't." I realized just how true those words were. Just as someone would not get upset at an infant for not being able to walk or talk, there was absolutely no reason to be upset with my mother when she could not follow easy directions. The first step, though, was learning to accept the new realities, which were always changing.

Truthfully, dementia was not a word that was on our radar; my mother suffered from macular degeneration and hearing loss, so it

Mrs. Miriam Goldberg (nee Lobel), a devoted wife, mother and grandmother, is a longtime resident of Southfield, Michigan (a suburb of Detroit). She is very grateful for her family's patience and understanding during those busy years of caring for Bubby. Their varied efforts to share in the care plan and visit Bubby both at home and at Fleishman's Residence were a tremendous source of encouragement and comfort.

was convenient to attribute certain behaviors to those handicaps – but eventually the symptoms worsened. My mother was a very intelligent and well-read woman. It was difficult for me to adjust to the new reality as her abilities declined. For example, it was so perplexing to me that my mother could be scammed multiple times by mail. I tried to point out that these offers were clearly scams, but it was a losing battle. (Unfortunately, the scammers know how to prey on a mind that is suffering from dementia.)

I began networking with friends who were caring for elderly parents and doing research. Slowly I came to the realization that my mother was no longer able to maintain a clean house and prepare meals. Sometimes she would forget to eat altogether.

A friend recommended an adult day care, which I checked out – I saw kind staff members working with clients who seemed much worse off than my mother. My gut reaction was that no, my mother certainly did not belong there. But as her abilities to perform meaningful tasks diminished and her need for recreation increased, I reconsidered, and I am so grateful that I did. My mother resisted going at first, and I felt like a mother bringing her nursery child to the first day of school, which was a devastating role reversal. I persisted, and she eventually spent many enjoyable hours there instead of staring at the walls at home. This was also an essential respite time for my stepfather, who was dealing with his own serious medical issues.

Undoubtedly, well-administered adult day-care centers are a wonderful resource.

A helpful tip from the earlier days, which can be used for those who are more aware, is to install a large clock/tablet that can be viewed from the person's bed, displaying the day of the week – Shabbos, in particular – besides the time. This is very helpful for many seniors who tend to be a little confused when they first awaken. It helps orient them easily without requiring them to ask anybody. This also helps them to avoid *chillul* Shabbos and the associated uncomfortable feelings.

There were times when my mother needed help with personal care and cleaning, and no caretaker was around, and I really struggled with this. Doing what had to be done seemed inappropriate for me as a daughter. One of the caretakers put this in a new light when she told me that they consider this an important part of their job, since it gives/restores the client's dignity. This really changed my perspective in this area.

As time went on, my mother's ability to talk became very compromised, but when I would sing/chant parts of *davening* or *zemiros* with her, the words would pour out and the happiness was reflected on her face. When someone would hold her hands, moving with her to the rhythm, it would help her focus and enjoy. We found it was helpful to say the words slowly and clearly – which I also realized was a wonderful way to encourage me to better focus on the words when I *davened*!

My brother sent video clips of himself singing her favorite *zemiros* – which could be played again and again and again – and which she could enjoy again and again and again – one of the positive aspects of her memory loss.

Something important I want to mention is that when visitors come to see someone with even mid-stage memory loss, it is best that they introduce themselves by name, followed by a short explanation. For example, "Hi! It's so good to see you! I'm your niece Golda, Hannah's daughter." This may or may not ring a bell, but it is far superior to, "Hi, of course you remember who I am!" followed by an uncomfortable silence. It was surprisingly common and painful to watch many well-meaning visitors fall into this uncomfortable situation.

During the last six months of her life, my mother lived in the dementia care unit of a Jewish facility, that, while kosher, catered mostly to a clientele that was not *frum*. Knowing that others would be dressing her, I tried not to pack any clothing that could be worn improperly, i.e., a low-necked sweater that would have to be worn with a shell or a sleeveless knit top meant to be worn under a cardigan.

I framed the following poem (which a friend helped me to pen) for her room. My mother was unable to advocate for herself or express her opinions, so this was helpful in reminding the staff (as well as the inevitable new aides) how she should be dressed; I found that the staff really tried to comply. I did need to find some different style head coverings, as some of the ones my mother had would slip off easily, and the staff could not be busy with constantly fixing them.

Hi! I'm Beth, it's so nice to meet you.
Your warmth and concern show in all that you do!
I can sense caring as you're helping me –
Making this room, my new home, a comfortable place to be.
Did you notice my paintings? I'm a woman of art.

You can access that still, singing straight to my heart.
Check out the song list for some songs that I know.
I can sing them with you, if you sing them really slow.
Feel free to try other songs – I may know them too.
Please add them to the list, for the rest of the crew.
I like to dress modestly, much like a queen,
My knees, elbows and collarbone never are seen.
Please help me keep to this dignified style,
You're sure to get used to it after a while.
When with company or out of my room I go,
My hair should be covered, it never should show.
It's a commitment to G-d I've kept since I was wed,
Please help me do this when I get out of my bed.
You are getting to know me, now that you've read
The things that I feel that I wish could be said.
With all of my heart, I thank you for caring
And look forward to happy times that we'll be sharing!

Since I mentioned to the programming director that my mother enjoyed *davening* and singing, she began *davening Adon Olam* with the group, and she was pleasantly surprised to see many others join in.

On one of my last visits to the facility to visit my mother before she succumbed to a short bout of pneumonia, my mother and I were walking down the hallway, she with her walker and me beside her, when she started mumbling, "*Keil Melech Ne'eman.*" In the earlier stages of her dementia, my mother would often say parts of *davening*, but as the disease progressed, she would generally repeat what others said rather than initiate words on her own, so this was out of the ordinary. I first thought she wanted to say *Shema*, so I began saying the paragraph of "*V'ahavta...*" but she continued to repeat, "*Keil Melech Ne'eman.*"

As I drove home from that visit, I heard my mother's voice telling me, "*Keil Melech Ne'eman* – Hashem knows what He is doing. We may not understand why some go through the journey of dementia, but Hashem is *Keil Melech Ne'eman*, He is a trustworthy G-d."

These were from the last words my mother said to me – may they continue to linger in my ears.

KEY POINTS:

- The first step in handling a patient's dementia is acknowledging and accepting the new reality.

- Adult day care can provide enjoyable socialization opportunities for the patient and essential respite for family members/caregivers.

- For early-stage memory loss: to help orient the patient, install a large clock near his/her bed displaying the day of the week and time (very helpful in reminding the patient about Shabbos).

- For mid-stage memory loss: encourage visitors to identify themselves by name and brief description (Hi, it's your niece Golda, Hannah's daughter).

- For women being cared for in a facility: remind staff members how to dress her modestly. Also, avoid sending garments that might be worn inappropriately (i.e., sweater set with sleeveless knit top, low-necked sweater requiring a shell).

- Let staff members know about specific activities the patient enjoys/is responsive to (i.e., singing, listening to music).

Final Due Date

Mrs. Miriam Klein Adelman

MY MOTHER IS LEAVING THIS WORLD. AND WE are absolutely and utterly helpless to stop it. We do not want her to leave, and as far as I know, she doesn't want to go either. At least when she was conscious she didn't want to. We talked then about her going home and how she would manage. She was concerned how she'd make suppers for Abba, how she'd take care of the house in her weakened state. *Halevai, you should get to that point,* I thought. Outwardly, I assured here that we would all still be around to help her until she got back on her feet.

Not long afterward she slipped into a coma, and since then, it's been guesswork. I have no idea what she's thinking or feeling now, if anything, and I so badly want to know. I wonder if her *neshamah* is hovering over her body like those out-of-body experiences I've read about, if it's observing us reciting Tehillim and talking amongst each other beside her bed. Some siblings are adamant that we include her in the conversation, others feel she's not cognizant of us any longer so why bother.

I want to know if she's already made contact with Hashem in a realer way than we normally do here on earth. If she's been visited by her deceased parents. I've heard many stories of after-death experiences. Only this isn't after death. Yet. This is right before death. Hours and moments inexorably moving closer to the end we know is coming.

In an eerie way this is like a birth. There, we don't know exactly when the baby will be born, when the *neshamah* will enter the world. Here, we don't know exactly when the *neshamah* will depart, although we do know the due date is around now. Will it be today? Tonight? When will the labor pains – the death throes – begin?

We all take turns staying with my mother at night and throughout the day. Tonight, as usual, we are all summoned to her bedside because "this is it." The doctors have predicted that she will not make it to the morning. This has gone on every night for the last few days. The entire family gathered each time by her bedside and said Tehillim. "It" never happened, so everybody, except the one whose turn it was to stay with her, left. Tonight it is my turn to sleep at the hospital, so I bed down on the couch in the corner. Every now and then my mother lets out a moan, as her body turns colder and makes its way toward the inevitable. I'm not nervous. Just numb. I'm going through the motions of a mature adult child dealing with her mother's passing. But I do not sleep much on that little couch in the corner.

I read a lot from *Mourning in Halachah* because if I do happen to be there the moment her *neshamah* leaves this world, I want to know what I'm supposed to say and do.

I've never confronted death before. Not in this intensely personal way. My grandparents passed away years ago, but they were old. My mother is only 73. They were two generations removed from me. I wasn't with them as they went through their death throes. *And they're not my mother.* My invincible mother, who never let the words "I can't" or "it's too hard" get in the way of doing what she felt was right. I cannot believe that she feels it's right to die and abandon us this way!

Morning has arrived. Is the sun peering through the window? A hint of a breeze in the air? Or is it a cloudy, windless day? I have no idea. My only world is the gray-walled, bare hospital room with the shell of the vibrant person I once knew, lying on the bed barely breathing. I hold her almost lifeless hand in mine. I stroke her arm and ask forgiveness.

I want so desperately to know what she is thinking and feeling as I apologize. To know if she believes I am truly sorry for not showing her proper respect. For the heartache I caused her as a teenager, especially now that I know what it's like to be a parent of teenagers. We did talk about this before she got sick. Not enough, though. Not nearly enough. I want to repair those loose ends in our relationship. But it is too late. I will never now know if she forgives me because she can no longer answer me.

There are visitors this morning. My father and sister come. The ever-faithful *bikur cholim* committee, doctors, nurses, and palliative care people stop by. Though most are compassionate, there are some insensitive ones. One woman from *bikur cholim* stops by, looks at my mother's inert form, my sister, father, and I huddled around her bed, smiles and airily says, "Oh, I'm sure everything will be fine." I want to slap her.

The orthopedic surgeon comes in to check her gangrenous leg. "We'll have to amputate," he says to us gravely. *Look at her face, man, she's half out of this world already!* I want to shout at him.

Shana, my 16-year-old daughter, has just arrived from out-of-town. We've been having ongoing, increasingly heated exchanges over the phone the past few days. She insisting she must come home to see Grandma, and I insisting it will be too late by the time she gets here, plus it's too expensive, plus it's in the middle of exam week. Shana wins. My husband picks her up at 7 a.m. at the airport and drops her off at the hospital.

Shana walks into the room and walks over to her grandmother. Does she say anything to her as she bends her head toward her, or does she simply sit silently by her bed? I can't tell. All I know is that Grandma has granted Shana her wish: Shana has seen her before she dies. In a few minutes, my shift is over.

I don't want to leave because I know death is so imminent. I realize I want to be with her at the very end. I want to be there to see the *Malach Hamaves* have the audacity to take her away from me. Nevertheless, Shana and I walk out of the room and into the elevator. We make it to the elevator and press the down button. As I step out, my sister calls me. *Baruch Dayan Ha'emes.*

Reprinted with permission from Mishpacha/Family First magazine. The author is writing under a pseudonym.

KEY POINTS:

- When someone is ill, death can mimic birth in that we don't know exactly when the *neshamah* will depart, although we are waiting for it to happen imminently.

- One might wonder whether a coma patient can hear what is being expressed at his/her bedside and whether the *neshamah* has yet made contact with the next world.

- When a loved one is declining, it is helpful to clear the air and ask forgiveness before it is too late.

Bitachon...
Or Denial?

As told to Rachel Schmidt, LCSW

I WAS FURIOUS AND BITTER. "MY HUSBAND DIED ON me," I moaned to the therapist. "He told me he'd get better, and he didn't. I will never forgive him."

My name is Freeda Kaufman, and five years after my husband passed away from pancreatic cancer I was still angry at him for lying to me. He kept telling me he'd get well. He promised. I spent my days crying and being depressed.

LET ME START FROM THE BEGINNING. SEVEN YEARS AGO, my husband went to the doctor with symptoms of nausea and lower

**Diagnosis...
and Betrayal**

back pain. The doctor took some blood tests and sent him home, saying it was a virus, and it would go away in a few days. It didn't. He went to the doctor again and did more bloodwork, which also came back fine. But the virus lingered, and he was losing weight. One morning, I noticed a slight yellow pallor to his face. It scared us both, so we immediately went to the emergency room. Two days later, more intensive bloodwork and the ultrasound confirmed our worst fears: pancreatic cancer.

My husband, Rabbi Kaufman, had always been a fighter. An only child born to Holocaust survivors who were already well into their forties, he matured early, having to care for his parents at a young age. He also felt a keen sense of responsibility to bring them *nachas* and joy. He studied hard and was a great student. He won the *mishnayos* contest and proudly brought home the shiny new bike that was

---

Rachel Schmidt is a licensed social worker and psychotherapist in private practice who specializes in child and adult evaluations. She is the author of Love is Not Enough (Targum Press, 2000) and A Rose Among Thorns (Israel Bookshop Publications, 2008). She is also an international lecturer on all topics relating to children and adults and can be heard on the Chazak Hotline.

132 / WHEN CARING COUNTS MOST

awarded as a prize. By the age of twenty he was married, and only two years later, he opened his own leasing company, edging out many seasoned companies by offering "impossible" prices to his customers. He then brought his semi-retired father into the business and later brought in two of his cousins, at-risk youths who gained a healthier perspective on life under his wise and sincere tutelage. My husband was what you call a hard worker, never taking a day of vacation in his life. He proved that diligence and hard work, coupled with G-d's blessing, could get you where you needed to be. There was almost nothing he couldn't do, from fixing a leaky faucet to learning with the most challenging *chavrusas*.

Our marriage was a good one, as he understood priorities. Our children, three boys and one girl, knew that they came first. He never missed a parent-teacher conference in school or a visiting day in camp. He was organized and prompt and diligent in attending *shiurim* and being on time for *minyan*. He even started a *minchah minyan* in his leasing company, which was attended by everyone on the block.

My husband was a doer who didn't include the word no in his dictionary and never took no for an answer. When the pancreatic cancer hit him like a ton of bricks, he threw himself into fighting it as he did everything else in life: completely and totally. He researched the disease until he became an expert and then announced that he would wage war with it until it surrendered. He gathered me and the children together and said confidently, "I have reached heights that others only dream about. This cancer is just another mountain to climb. With a lot of *davening*, hard work, and Hashem's help, I will overcome this challenge."

He was so convincing that I believed him. He underwent surgery, but they were not able to remove all of the cancer. After months of chemotherapy and radiation he was not doing much better and was never quite able to go into remission. Still, he did not give up. He reached out to *rebbes* and *gedolim* of various stripes all over the world. They all gave him *chizzuk* and blessed him for a *refuah sheleimah*. One *rebbe* advised him to buy a new pair of *tefillin* written by a certain *tzaddik* in Israel. Another told him to sleep in his *tzitzis*, and a third suggested that he not talk on Shabbos to avoid the possibility of *lashon hara*. He also took upon himself to recite the entire *sefer* Tehillim every morning, which was often almost impossible to do as his health deteriorated drastically in spite of all the *berachos*.

He never even said goodbye to me. Until the very end, he insisted he was going to beat the cancer. Any time I looked concerned or sighed, he would say, "G-d will help. *Bitachon! Bitachon!* Where is your *bitachon?*"

Other times, he would note my worried look and chirp like a cheerleader, "Freeda, don't think negatively. Think positive. Remember, the *rabbanim* promised that we would dance at the weddings of our grandchildren, and none of our four children are married yet."

Then he would go *daven* some more. He made no contingency plans for the future whatsoever.

The Fallout

AS A RESULT, THE LEASING COMPANY IS NOW GONE. After he passed away, my sons, with no clear direction, began to argue among themselves, each claiming to own more of the business than the others. The oldest son said that since he was the *bechor*, the firstborn, he deserved more; the second said he had worked three summers in the business and hadn't drawn a salary: the youngest said he once lent the company $20,000 and was never paid back. I demanded that they sell it and divide the money evenly, which they did.

Well, five years later I still felt enraged. My hardworking, capable husband, who had always accomplished everything he set out to do, had convinced himself that he would beat an almost incurable illness. All of the medical literature stated that the survival rate for pancreatic cancer was one to three years. But my husband, who was used to moving mountains, was sure that he could move the cancer out of his system.

Throughout it all, I had deep questions but hesitated to voice them. In fact, I was ashamed to. I couldn't sleep nights, wondering whether his tough approach was coming from a place of sincere *bitachon* or from a place of arrogance that assumed he could do anything. Was he really fighting the disease or was he just denying it? There's a fine line between the two, and I was never sure about the truth.

Years later I was still in deep pain, begging to be heard. I needed to express the feelings in my heart that had been kept hidden for so long. Maybe my husband had been too fixated on fighting at the expense of accepting. Hadn't Ya'akov Avinu *davened* that people should become sick before death in order to give us a chance to tidy up our personal and business matters before leaving this world? When Ya'akov Avinu gave the *berachos* to his sons, wasn't it a way of saying farewell and giving his children closure? If my husband had really been so wise and *ehrlich*, why hadn't he done the same?

I knew I couldn't go on like this and decided to see a therapist, someone to whom I could express my conflicting emotions. I couldn't pretend I was fine anymore. My wonderful husband, who had taken care of the whole world, had left his own family stranded.

In the therapist's office I sat in a chair, whining like a small child. "We never said goodbye to each other," I sobbed. "He was sick for eighteen months and just left me without a word."

What the therapist told me was interesting. She said that she herself didn't know what she would have done had she been in my husband's shoes. Perhaps she would have also continued to fight even after the battle was lost, refusing to surrender to G-d's will. At the same time, if she were in my shoes, she would also feel resentful of my husband's refusal to face the reality of his prognosis and betrayed by his stubborn unwillingness to tie up all the loose ends of his affairs. I found it amazing that she was able to understand both points of view at the same time.

I couldn't believe how well the therapist articulated my feelings. I had been waiting for five years to unburden myself.

In retrospect I was able to see that when that particular *rebbe* told my husband to get a new pair of *tefillin*, it wasn't a guarantee, but rather, a *zechus*, and it was the same with all the other rabbis. They had all give him *berachos* and *bentched* him that Hashem should answer his prayers, and He had – the answer was no. You cannot live longer than the number of years allotted to you. Moshe Rabbeinu couldn't change Hashem's decree that he would pass away before entering Eretz Yisrael, and neither could my husband. Unlike Moshe Rabbeinu, though, who eventually accepted the decree, my husband, a fighter till the end, never surrendered to G-d's will. He denied his prognosis even after cancer had spread to almost every part of his body. When his kidneys shut down and he was swollen with water, he insisted that he was going to have a *yeshuah*. He kept saying, "Watch and see. Hashem is going to perform His miracle now." He died waiting for the miracle to happen.

Paying the Price of Denial

THE THERAPIST TOLD ME SHE UNDERSTOOD MY anguish. Unfortunately, my husband wasn't the first person who refused to accept his prognosis. She had seen many people deny their illnesses (both physical and emotional) and in the process destroy the lives of their loved ones.

She told me about a sixteen-year-old girl who had been in denial about her anorexia. Although her bones stuck out and she looked like a skeleton, she insisted that she was merely watching her weight because she didn't want to get fat. Even when she collapsed and was hospitalized for malnutrition, she denied her illness and insisted that she was fine – and had only another five pounds to lose before she reached her goal.

She paid a horribly high price for her denial, and she died in her sleep from a heart attack. Ten years later, her family is still in mourning.

I learned that denial is a luxury that comes with a stiff price.

Although it was good to finally articulate my feelings, it took me a while to assimilate everything fully. It was no wonder I was angry that my husband had insisted he would recover in the face of all evidence to the contrary. A person is supposed to have *bitachon*, but he's also not supposed to depend on miracles. One should surely *daven* for a *refuah sheleimah*, but does that mean ignoring stark medical evidence? A human being can only be in charge of his *hishtadlus*, but he cannot control the outcome.

Finally Free to Mourn

I WORKED WITH THE THERAPIST FOR A WHILE. IT TOOK a lot of time and effort. Before I could begin to mourn the loss of my husband, I had to mourn the loss of his integrity. It was only after I had given voice to my anger, disappointment, and sense of betrayal that I was able to move on and grieve the loss of a most wonderful husband. I cried remembering the *kavanah* he had while making *kiddush*. With great pride I recalled his respect for all mankind, regardless of race or religion. I also shared with my therapist the stack of warm and personal birthday and anniversary cards he had given me over the years. I was happy to see that my memories of my husband no longer evoked an avalanche of anger, but rather, a sense of warmth. I knew I was making progress.

"You know," I whispered one day, "I never removed his clothes from the closet. They're still there as if he's coming home tomorrow. Even his hat is still on the dresser where he put it. I think I'm going to box them up today and send them to a *gemach*."

My husband's character was ultimately restored for me, enabling me to get past my pain and replace it with positive memories. As termination of my therapy grew near, I knew that I was ready to move on, toward a future that was hopefully filled with new beginnings.

I had finally learned to forgive.

Reprinted from To Fill the Sky with Stars, with permission from Menucha Publishers.

KEY POINTS:

- There is a fine line between *bitachon* and denial of reality. A person can only control his *hishtadlus*, not the final outcome.

- It is not uncommon for those facing devastating illness to deny the degree of their sickness and/or their prognosis. Unfortunately, denial can have painful ramifications for those left behind.

- When struggling with unresolved feelings of anger and resentment toward a loved one after their death, it can be important to speak with a professional to learn to move past the anger and grieve the actual loss.

- Being able to forgive a loved one when feeling betrayed is key to being able to move on with one's life.

CHAPTER IV

Protecting Yourself and Your Loved Ones:
Advice and Legal Guidance

Introduction To Estate Planning Documents

Mr. Ronald A. Spirn, ESQ.

THE PURPOSE OF THIS ARTICLE IS TO PROVIDE AN understanding of the essential estate-planning documents every adult should consider having. However, before discussing estate-planning documents, we should first define what is meant by the term "estate planning." Many people think that estate planning is about taxes and is only for wealthy people. Some with additional knowledge would say it is about inheritances. Although both responses are correct, they are only a small part of the answer. In fact, as we will see further in this article, several estate-planning documents are meant to be utilized only during a person's lifetime and have nothing to do with what happens after the person's death. The documents that will be covered in this article are: Powers of Attorney, Health Care Proxies and Living Wills, Last Wills and Testament (and Trusts).

Power Of Attorney

A POWER OF ATTORNEY ("POA") IS A LEGAL DOCUMENT with which the person making the POA gives authority to one or more individuals to make legal and financial decisions on his behalf. The person who creates the POA is called the "principal;" the person who is being

Mr. Ronald A. Spirn, JD, CELA, is the managing shareholder of Ronald A. Spirn, P.C., with offices in Cedarhurst, New York. Ronald earned his law degree at Yeshiva University's Benjamin N. Cardozo School of Law in 1993. His areas of practice include Elder Law, Medicaid Eligibility, Asset-Protection Planning, Nursing Home and Home-Care Issues, Estate-Tax Planning, Special-Needs Planning, Wills and Trusts, Guardianship and Probate and Administration of decedents' estates. In his twenty-five years as an Elder Law attorney, Mr. Spirn has helped over 3000 clients.

appointed is the "agent." There are several different provisions that can be included in the POA, including specifying the conditions under which the Agent(s) may act. The main point is that if a person does not have a POA and they are no longer able to manage their legal or financial affairs, no one will be able to step in and do so without a highly involved and complicated court proceeding known as a guardianship.

By setting up the POA in advance of an incapacitating event, the principal is stating his wishes as to whom it should be that will step up and take over. This could be a spouse if there is one that is capable of doing so; or it could be a child or other relative. The most important thing above all else is that the Agent is trustworthy. The Agent under the POA does not have medical decision making authority. When the principal dies, the POA ceases to be valid and can no longer be used.

Health Care Proxy/ Living Will

THE SAME WAY THAT THERE IS A DOCUMENT FOR substitute decision making for finances, there are also legal documents that can be set up so that an agent can make medical decisions on behalf of the principal if he is unable to communicate his wishes to others. A Health Care Proxy is a document which appoints another individual who can make substitute medical decisions on the principal's behalf if the principal is unable to do so.

When it comes to end of life decision making, the agent must know the principal's wishes which can either be communicated in writing or expressed verbally to the Agent. If the wishes are in writing, this would be a Living Will. There are both secular and "*halachic*" living wills. The main difference between the two is that the *halachic* version names a rabbinical authority who is to be consulted for any life and death questions that arise and the secular version does not. The two kinds of forms will also differ as to various types of medical treatment that may be provided or withheld. Again, just like with the POA, if a person does not have a Medical Proxy or Living Will and crucial medical decisions need to be made, a guardianship proceeding may need to be commenced.

A LAST WILL AND TESTAMENT (OR "WILL") IS A DOCUMENT
which a person establishes in order to direct how his estate assets

Last Will and Testament should pass upon his death. A person's estate is comprised of bank accounts, brokerage accounts, real estate holdings, business interests and many other forms of property. Numerous special provisions can be added to meet the specific needs of the one making a Will. The person creating a Will is called a "Testator." The Testator also names his Executor in the Will. The Executor is the person who takes care of all of the deceased person's estate matters after death. Wills do not apply to assets that have a co-owner or a designated beneficiary.

The Will has no effect while the Testator is alive and only takes effect upon his death. If a person dies without a Will, then they have died "intestate." When this happens, the estate will pass in accordance with a set of laws that may not be what the person intended. In addition, since there is no Will, no one has been named Executor so a number of individuals could try to assume control of the estate. This could of course lead to strife among family members. For this and many other reasons, it is preferable that a Will be done. A Will cannot be made on someone else's behalf.

THERE IS AN ALTERNATIVE ESTATE PLANNING DOCUMENT
that many individuals choose instead of a Last Will and Testament.

Living Trusts That document is a Trust. A Will states what happens with a person's estate after death. The Will must be submitted to the Probate or Surrogate's Court where the deceased person was living in order to have an Executor appointed who would then carry out the instructions contained in the Will. This process can take anywhere from a few to many months.

Living Trusts, sometimes referred to as *inter vivos* trusts, as the name indicates, are established during a person's lifetime. Otherwise, if a person writes their Will and has trust provisions contained in the Will which only take effect after the person dies, this would be known as a "testamentary trust."

When a person sets up a Trust, there is no need to go to court in order to have an Executor appointed. This is because the Trust states who is being appointed as the Trustee of the Trust who must follow the terms of the Trust, but without the need for court involvement.

The decision to use a Trust as the main estate vehicle instead of a Will can be based upon any number of reasons.

Using a Trust can provide greater privacy than a Will which becomes public record. If heirs live out of state (or even out of the country) or if there is property held by the deceased in different states, a Trust is more suitable. Another reason to set up a Trust could be if there may be any unhappy family members who may want to contest the estate for any reason. Since the Trust does not have to go through a court process in order to be effective like a Will does, there is no opportunity given to dispute the Trust's validity or the appointment of the Trustee, as there is when a Will is submitted to court for probate.

Living Trusts can be set up for a variety of reasons. Wealthy individuals may use a Trust for tax or family succession planning. Trusts can also be used in order to shelter assets from creditors or in the context of Medicaid planning. And as stated above, Trusts can be utilized solely in order to avoid probate.

In order to establish an appropriate estate plan and determine what the necessary legal documents are for you, the advice of an experienced estate planning attorney should be sought.

KEY POINTS:

- Estate planning is important for everyone, no matter their financial circumstances.

- **Power of Attorney (POA)** gives authority to one or more individuals to make legal and financial decisions on behalf of the **principal** (the person setting up the POA) should the principal become incapacitated.

- **Health Care Proxy/Living Will** appoints an individual to make medical decisions on the principal's behalf should the principal be unable to do so.

- A **Halachic Living Will** differs from a secular Living Will in that it names a rabbinical authority to be consulted for life-and-death decisions.

- A **Last Will and Testament** establishes how one's estate assets should be distributed upon his death. The person creating the will is a **Testator**. The person responsible for the Testator's estate after his death is the **Executor**.

- If a person dies without a will, he has died **intestate**.

- It is important that a will be drawn up to prevent family strife or assets from being distributed contrary to what the deceased desired.

- **Living Trusts** are established during a person's lifetime and do not require court involvement.

- A Living Trust may be set up for a number of reasons, including tax or family succession planning; to shelter assets from creditors; or in the context of Medicaid planning.

Ensuring the Safety and Security of Loved Ones Being Cared for by an Aide

Mr. David Cohen

A S A *FRUM* PRIVATE INVESTIGATOR PRACTICING since the 1990s, I have been repeatedly called to consult on cases involving aides. The purpose of this article is to provide an overview of the issues involved and provide practical suggestions to ensure the safety of loved ones.

Families typically bring in a caretaker when they live a long distance from the patient, or when the patient requires constant care that family members are unable to accommodate. There are two categories of caregivers: those with certification, such as CNA (Certified Nursing Assistant), and those who are unlicensed home health aides. The difference between them is that CNAs are trained in first aid, CPR, taking vital signs and maintaining records. In home settings, both types are usually expected to prepare meals and medications and assist with dressing, bathing and outside activities, i.e. walks, visits to doctors. Some families also ask the aide to clean the home, do laundry and/or shop for perishable items such as milk and eggs.

There are instances in which a paid caregiver is a family member. This article, for the most part, assumes that the hired aide is a "stranger." As trusting as we are and want to be, we need to remember that we never fully know *who* the aide is and what s/he is capable of. While

---

Mr. David Cohen is a private investigator with thirty years of experience in the field. He lives in Baltimore, Maryland.

individuals drawn to caregiving are usually loving and compassionate people, some are scheming, larcenous and cruel individuals looking to take advantage of vulnerable, elderly or sick individuals. Within that continuum are a wide range of problematic scenarios, including individuals suffering from depression or mental illness who are lax or inattentive; domineering personalities who act like drill sergeants ordering vulnerable patients around; and caregivers who are physically and/or verbally abusive.

MANY PROBLEMS CAN BE AVOIDED BY DOING SIMPLE due diligence before hiring. If one hires a person from a licensed,

Preventive Measures reputable agency whose workers are licensed and bonded, the onus of due diligence is on the agency. If you are hiring on your own, we suggest taking the following measures: 1) Call the candidate's references and ask both open-ended and targeted questions about the caregiver's work ethic, level of caring, honesty and integrity. Listen carefully to what is being said and ask follow-up questions if you hear any hesitancy on the reference's part. 2) If the references are good, it is important to conduct a basic criminal and civil background check to see if the candidate has a negative history of suspicious activity. There are online services that conduct checks on potential employees, some of which are more comprehensive. A private investigator can also be hired. 3) Interview the candidate in person. It is important to assess the candidate's presentation: Did s/he come on time? Is s/he well groomed – neat, properly dressed, clean? 4) During the interview, it is important to verify whether the candidate is up to the job. If the patient requires specific medical protocols or use of specific medical equipment, is the aide trained to do this? It is helpful to pose mock scenario questions to ascertain what the aide would do in a particular situation. The mock scenarios should mirror the job. Thus, if the patient has dementia and wanders away, is incontinent, or becomes verbally abusive, it is important to see whether the aide is prepared for these situations and how s/he would respond. 5) Finally – and most importantly – requesting proof of one's CNA license, passport, social-security card, immigration papers and/or driver's license are the most reliable due-diligence methods. Make sure to photocopy these so that you have a way of tracing the individual should there be an issue. And make sure to keep the photocopies *outside* the home so that the aide does not abscond with the file.

As care becomes more complex, multiple shifts are needed. Obviously, the due diligence required for multiple aides is that much more complex. There is often rivalry between aides, which further adds to the complexity. It is always best when multiple aides get along and are singly focused on the welfare of their charge.

None of these preventive measures are iron-clad guarantees. I have been involved with cases where aides with blemish-free records succumbed to temptation and stole valuables. Security experts agree that we can never totally protect – the best we can do is prevent and deter. In this regard, it is prudent to avoid temptation. Valuables and cash should always be locked up. Wealth and possessions should never be flaunted. Aides must never have power of attorney or the ability to sign checks. Relatives and patients should refrain from giving aides access to bank accounts, checkbooks, credit cards, safety-deposit box keys and mail.

With regard to family documents, aides should be restricted from having access to wills and inheritances. The executor should be a family member. All documents that have been changed from what was previously executed with the knowledge of the family should be inspected for possible forged signatures.

On a different note, hired help should not be allowed to bring their relatives or friends to the home. This could be a red flag and invite unscrupulous people into the home. Alarm systems, doorbell cameras, chain locks and peepholes should be in place to guard against intrusion or burglary. Vacation plans should be kept private, in the event aides are working in conjunction with potential burglars.

Hired help should also be instructed regarding visitors and volunteer do-gooders. This is a delicate issue, as on the one hand, visitors can be valuable "outside eyes"; on the other hand, they can be intrusive and can interfere with patient care. A trusted aide should be empowered to monitor visitors and protect the patient. When *bikur cholim* and caring neighbors and friends visit, it should be noted who these people are, when they visit and what happens during the visit. Do they know their boundaries? Are they friendly visitors or are they interfering with prescribed medical care? Protecting fragile patients from germs is very important to patient safety. Have they been advised not to visit if they have cold symptoms, feel under the weather, or are running a slight fever?

It is extremely important to compensate employees fairly for their services and to treat them respectfully. Respect, decent compensation, reasonable job descriptions, vacation days and holiday gifts go a long way. A satisfied employee is less likely to engage in illicit activity and more likely to protect their client in a diligent manner. Happy, well-compensated employees are motivated to go beyond their strict duties. Thus, for example, I have seen motivated aides protect their naïve charges from telephone scammers who would have otherwise defrauded them.

ELECTRONIC MONITORING HAS BECOME A COMMON practice. It is standard in many homes – and in many daycare settings and early-childhood classrooms – to have a

Monitoring – A Must Today

"nanny cam" that records and has both audio and video capabilities. The presence of these cameras is openly shared with the aide. Honest aides do not object to a nanny cam. If an open system is not an option, one has many monitoring options. Security companies can implement covert cameras in your home to track caretaker activity. If this service is too expensive, one can purchase covert cameras online for reduced prices. Private investigators also sell devices such as alarm-clock cameras that can covertly monitor activity. Some of these products have voice activation that can record verbal abuse.

My private detective experience has included elder-abuse investigations. One case unfortunately resulted in the illicit drainage of hundreds of thousands of dollars in monetary funds and property from an elderly woman's account in Pennsylvania. These activities were promoted by a family court judge scheming with a court-appointed guardian and physician who intentionally mistreated, misrepresented and misdiagnosed the victim. Similar corrupt activity, while not common, has surfaced in various states throughout America. One recommendation for stopping such activity is placing checks and balances, or so-called monitoring procedures, in place throughout the family court system, hiring an unbiased liaison to select honest guardians and physicians.

SECURITY EXPERTS AGREE THAT THERE ARE ALWAYS telltale signs of abuse and neglect. Employees who are constantly **Danger** complaining and/or patients who appear in distress and **Signs** who are lacking proper health/hygiene are warning signs that an aide is failing to complete their assigned tasks. Suspicious packages and unexpected deliveries are also warning signs of possible danger.

The first cause for alarm is the patient's own complaint – or, in more serious cases, a change of personality from talkative to fearful and reticent. On the phone one should ask the patient: Are you afraid? Is the aide listening in?

If there is any question, a friendly neighbor, the synagogue rabbi, a local social worker specializing in geriatrics or a private investigator should be called in to check on the situation. If there is suspicion of serious criminal or dangerous behavior, police (911) should be called. Better to trust an instinct or gut reaction than to be fooled and subject your loved one to bodily or psychological harm.

Complicating the picture of disturbing patient self-reporting is what happens when patients suffer from dementia, or when they are trauma survivors, including Holocaust victims. These individuals often suffer from paranoia and fear of strangers. Thus, many elderly patients will complain that their attendants are stealing from them, whispering behind their backs, mistreating them, overdosing them, poisoning their food and/or starving them. Some will spin convoluted tales that have no basis in reality.

It is always important to listen carefully and to err on the side of caution. In these cases particularly, electronic monitoring is a wonderful way to ascertain the truth.

Life happens. Fragile elderly individuals will fall and get bruised or break bones. Occasionally a weary attendant who was up all night might sleep late. If the patient is very difficult, the attendant might even lose their patience and yell. It is important to remember that elderly patients will deteriorate because this is the nature of aging. Caretakers are human and cannot be expected to do better than a patient's own family member would do under trying circumstances. The key is to ensure that the aide is doing the best s/he can, and that the patient is being taken care of in a competent and caring way.

A PRIVATE INVESTIGATOR WILL PROVIDE A
comprehensive background check for approximately $200.
What Will This Cost Surveillance on a caregiver typically costs $100 to $150 an hour; there are those who will charge as little as $65. There is a cottage industry of geriatric social workers in retirement communities such as Florida who can serve as family surrogates and perform on-site caregiver monitoring and due diligence. Social worker fees are generally monthly, and vary widely based on a wide range of factors, including the intensity of monitoring involved, and the experience of the social worker.

Sadly, private investigators are called into complex family disputes regarding care. Increasingly, with certain states funding family members to be caretakers, caretakers are relatives, children, grandchildren, siblings, nieces, nephews or cousins. Hopefully, there is understanding and coordinated communication between family members. Unfortunately, sometimes family members disagree, or even worse, are antagonistic, pathological and dysfunctional, in which case the patient and/or caregiver or both become victims of family crossfire. Money and inheritance issues may underlie the tension. When family members disagree on care, the matter is often brought to secular court (which is a *chillul Hashem*) and *dinei Torah*. In these cases, there is often a need for a court-appointed guardian. Every effort should be made to avoid conflicts reaching this level by seeking wise *da'as Torah* (rabbinical guidance).

PEACE OF MIND IS CRUCIAL FOR THE RECIPIENT OF
care and family members. Being alert and following the aforementioned
Conclusion recommendations is our *hishtadlus* (effort) in preventing criminal or otherwise unlawful activity and ensuring that our loved ones are receiving excellent and compassionate care.

KEY POINTS:

- When hiring outside home-health aides, there are two kinds of employees: CNA – Certified Nursing Assistant and unlicensed home-health aides.

- Most aides are loving and compassionate, but there are those bad apples who try to take advantage of elderly, ill or vulnerable individuals.

- If not hiring an aide through an agency, be sure to carefully research the candidate before hiring.

- Call references and ask open-ended targeted questions.

- Conduct a basic criminal and civil background check.

- Interview the candidate in person. When doing so, verify that the candidate is capable of doing what is required for the job.

- Most importantly, request proof of the candidate's CNA license, passport, social-security card, immigration papers and/or driver's license. Photocopy identification papers and keep copies of them outside the home.

- Even aides with a blemish-free record can succumb to temptation. Take the necessary precautions to protect valuables and assets.

- Aides should be restricted from having access to wills and inheritances.

- Install appropriate safeguards and surveillance equipment. Electronic monitoring can be helpful in tracking caretaker activity.

- The aide should be given instructions regarding outside visitors.

- It is very important to compensate employees fairly and to treat them decently. Happy employees are motivated to go beyond their designated duties.

- Private investigators and/or social workers can be hired to properly vet potential aides and/or explore the possibility of misconduct.

- Look out for signs of abuse and neglect. First cause for alarm is the patient's complaint or any change in personality.

- Although patient reports can be complicated by dementia or a history of trauma, it is important to err on the side of caution and take the necessary steps to verify the situation.

- When family members are caregivers, there can sometimes be underlying tension and disagreements about care. It is important to seek guidance from *da'as Torah* to avoid conflict.

- The key is always to ensure that the patient is being cared for in a competent, caring way.

The Right to Live:

A LOOK AT THE LEGAL RIGHTS IN END-OF-LIFE SITUATIONS AND HOW TO BEST EQUIP YOURSELF IN ADVANCE

Mr. Mark J. Kurzmann, ESQ.

D ISCUSSING OUR OWN MORTALITY OR THAT of our loved ones can be tremendously frightening. It is easier not to dwell on this natural part of life, so much so that we might almost deny that it will ever happen to us or those close to us. However, when we don't address the very important matters related to end-of-life circumstances, the ramifications can be very serious.

We should all live long and healthy lives. But what happens if an emergency does arise?

Brain death. Familiar words to most people. But when these words are said about one's own family member, so many questions arise. What does the term really mean? What does one need to be aware of? What about those stories of hospitals wanting to pull the plug?

THE CONCEPT OF BRAIN DEATH ORIGINATED DECADES ago, once technology was able to detect if there is activity in the brain.

Brain Death: A Dangerous Diagnosis If the brain is not, so to speak, "alive," a person can't function and will die very shortly. However, today there are machines and medicines that will support the body even if the brain is dead.

Another very significant factor is that today, doctors can harvest and transplant vital organs such as the kidney, heart, liver and lungs. Previously skin and corneas were the only organs that could be transplanted.

Mr. Mark J. Kurzmann, Esq., is a former US Department of Justice national security and civil litigator now in private practice. He has advocated for patients across the country in end-of-life and related matters and has spoken on the subject extensively. He is also one of the few American lawyers who attended the Edmond Sarfa murder trial in Monaco.

There is a major problem with this new reality: we can't harvest an organ from someone who is still alive, and we can't kill someone to obtain an organ. It is arguable if the original heart transplants performed in Africa were actually murders. The "dead donor rule" is an ethical constraint that categorically prohibits causing death by organ removal. This informal rule has guided the practice of organ transplantation since its inception. However, the rule also says that brain death, the irreversible cessation of all brain function, is considered equivalent to death. Today, if a donor is declared brain dead even if the heart is pumping and the person is breathing naturally or with machines, doctors don't consider it murder to unplug the machines sustaining him.

There are studies that have been done about the inconsistencies of the tests hospitals use to decide if a person is brain dead or not. The philosophy behind all this is basically: let's harvest organs and keep a young person alive rather than keep an essentially dead person alive. If the person is not conscious and is thus not a member of society anymore, he is no better than a vegetable, so we don't need him. But no hospital test can determine if there was a *yetzi'as neshamah*.

This creates many difficulties for families that want to keep their loved ones alive.

How do we enforce patients' and families' rights for medical care when the patient is at the end of life and there are *halachic* parameters regarding the definition of "death"?

THERE ARE TWO VERY IMPORTANT STEPS THAT SHOULD be taken: 1) Make sure that you have the proper documents signed, including the healthcare proxy and pocket-size EMES Card, [*Ed. Note: See sample EMES card on page 219.*] which informs people that you have a healthcare proxy and have filled out the necessary forms. 2) Speak to your family members about signing the documents as well. You might think you'll take care of it "when the time comes" – whether that means when diagnosed with an illness or when admitted to a hospital, etc. But one does not always have notice about the onset of these circumstances. And even if you are not facing an emergency situation, you may not be in the position to sign all the documents you are handed with a clear head. I recently

Healthcare Proxy and EMES Card

had an MRI, which lasted only a few hours, but before I went in, I was handed a stack of forms. It wasn't possible to read through them all before signing if I wanted to keep my appointment. What too often happens is that people sign documents without even realizing what they are agreeing to. Is it uncomfortable to talk with your spouse or elderly parents about this? Yes. Is it okay to wait for that "perfect moment" to talk about it? No, because that "perfect moment" usually doesn't happen.

There is a philosophical view that is embodied in our country's laws relating to these matters, and that is the premise that I am the *ba'al habayis* of my own body and I can decide if I want to take medicine or not, or if I want to live or not. This is contrary to the Torah's view. Unfortunately, this mindset has opened the door for *frum* people to say, "I believe that I am dead under x circumstances."

The modern redefining of death as "brain dead" has become the source of a great deal of controversy and stress to many members of the observant community regardless of whether or not a particular patient and his religious values are consistent with criteria for brain death; in many instances after the patient can't speak for him or herself, hospital staff will request of the family to conduct any of a series of confirmatory tests, which have been shown to be inconsistent and even harmful. In our experience, the emotional strain of being asked this question when the loved one is incapable of speaking up for him or herself can be physically and emotionally unbearable. The choice between acquiescing or refusing to acquiesce to such a request by the medical staff caring for one's loved one is nearly impossible to handle or navigate. Therefore, it behooves us to consult with a knowledgeable rabbinic authority as to how to handle such an unfortunate situation while we are well and not experiencing emotional distress.

WITH PROPER PLANNING, WE CAN AVOID UNCERTAINTY regarding how to proceed if we or our loved ones should ever, *chas v'Shalom*, find ourselves in these circumstances. A

Speak to a Rav person should consult with a *rav* who is well-versed in the applicable laws in the relevant states and will take into account factors such as *kavod haberiyos* as well; this will enable him to instruct his family or other proxy or agent about what kinds of treatments he does or does not desire, within the bounds of *halachah*.

If he specifically doesn't wish to suffer with prolonged pain, or conversely, wants his life prolonged as much as possible even through great pain, he can let the proxy know this. Again, as this subject is not clear cut, it must be discussed with a *rav*; in addition, the correct agents must be selected. It is important to make your wishes very clear and to make sure the chosen proxy clearly understands those wishes. And it is important to speak to a *rav* who is knowledgeable about all this not only when facing a medical situation, but when signing the proxy forms.

Prominent *poskim* have recognized the right of each individual *choleh* to instruct their healthcare agent or family to avoid treatment that will prolong their suffering. A person is not obligated to experience pain indefinitely. But there is a fine line between doing what is required by *halachah* to keep a person alive and reducing their suffering, and there are specific *rabbanim* who have expertise in this area.

Make Sure Your Wishes are Known

I HAD A RELATIVE WHO WAS ON A VENTILATOR FOR over ten years. During that time, he seemed to be experiencing great pain. I conferenced together with this *choleh*'s family and their *rav*. One of the grandchildren was a highly trained radiologist, and one of the questions I asked was if it was possible to detect whether the person was suffering or not. That being said, he had never told us if he wanted to suffer for longer to merit more *Olam Haba*. It is important for every individual to think about how much pain they would want to experience. Many *poskim* will take into consideration the patient's pain *and* if they preferred to live longer with more pain.

A Growing Need

WE ARE LIVING DURING A TIME OF GREAT LEGAL RIGHTS, as well as great technological advances that can support one's *halachic* position. The baby-boomer generation is a large, healthy population, but as the years go by, the circumstances in which these issues will need to be addressed will increase exponentially.

I think that everyone ages 18 and up should have a healthcare proxy, EMES Card and *halachic* will properly signed. This is so important that at the risk of sounding like a real fanatic, I think that the *klal* should come together and say, "Unless you have the forms signed, the *rav* can't sell your *chametz* or you can't buy seats in *shul* for the *Yamim Nora'im*."

The necessary forms to assign a healthcare proxy are easily attainable from either Agudath Israel, with a dropdown box for each state that ensures the laws from that state are covered, or from the Rabbinic Council of America.

Unlike a will, a healthcare proxy does not need to be notarized. The only condition is that it must be signed before two witnesses. Once you have your proxy filled out, you can make as many copies as you wish and distribute them to as many people as you wish.

Israel is decades beyond us in this respect, and the importance of signing such forms is taken very seriously there. They have created a government website where the forms can be signed, and they are kept on file electronically. Any doctor can search for this information for any patient, and the forms must be updated every five years.

In New Jersey, there is a law that allows people not to accept brain death as the definition of death on religious grounds, so that they can treat their loved ones as alive until there is cardio-respiratory criterion. There is no wiggle room for hospitals in this regard. In one case in which I was involved, brain-death confirmatory tests were performed against the patient's family's wishes, and the hospital entered her as dead. But we fought this, and they ultimately revoked the time of death. To our knowledge, such a change has never been successfully discharged before.

In New York the law is much broader and provides that the staff can keep a person on machines for what they consider reasonable accommodations. A patient I knew was hospitalized in New York, and on Shavuos morning, when the doctors knew the family could not make any phone calls, they performed a brain-death confirmatory test against the family's wishes. The patient was pronounced dead, and a death certificate was issued. I called up the hospital lawyers on Shavuos morning and was on the phone with them for an hour to reverse that. They did agree to reverse it and transferred him to another hospital. The patient lived for another three weeks and was *niftar* at the time Hashem decreed.

I am involved now with the case of a very sick woman who signed an organ-donor card. Based on her medical condition, it is very possible that when she signed, she didn't know what she was agreeing to; unfortunately, her designation as an organ donor is probably written on her driver's license. Her family is *frum* and doesn't want her to be a donor. The problem is, if she signed the organ-donor card, she loses her right to *halachically* acceptable treatment after her demise. We tried very hard to reach a compromise that would be *halachically* acceptable but have been unsuccessful.

The fact is, fighting what the documents state (or don't state) after the fact is very difficult. As difficult as it might be to initiate a conversation on this subject with a non-*frum* relative, it is so important to take care of it to avoid these situations.

I HAD AN UNCLE WHO APPOINTED MY COUSIN TO BE HIS healthcare agent. When he was hospitalized for the first time, I went to the hospital with the healthcare proxy and asked his doctor, who happened to be *frum,* what to do with the healthcare proxy document. He told me to give it to the nurse, which I did. A year later, my uncle was admitted to that hospital again. I told the nurse that a proxy had been submitted, and she should make sure to have it on hand. To my dismay, it was nowhere to be found. The nurse explained that the proper way to submit it was through admissions. I drove an hour to my office, got another copy, drove straight back to the hospital and went to admissions. I handed the document to the nurse, who told me she would take care of it. I politely, but firmly told her, "Please can you take care of this now? It is really important to me." And she did it as I watched.

Submit Documents Correctly

So have the healthcare proxy, have multiple copies and make sure it is submitted correctly when necessary.

When there is a divergence between the patient's religious rights and the hospital's medical judgment about how the patient should be treated or not treated, and the matter can't be worked out formally, then the family has a right to meet the ethics committee. These situations are extremely delicate, time-sensitive and emotionally wrenching. However, it is important to remain calm when speaking to doctors. Losing oneself and yelling is only counterproductive.

I am not an extremist, but based on the tragedies I have seen and the tragedies I have helped avert, I know firsthand that establishing a knowledgeable *rav* and signing the necessary paperwork are of vital importance. It is my hope that this article opens people's eyes to the utmost necessity of addressing these matters.

KEY POINTS:

- Brain death is a term used to describe the lack of activity in the brain. Today, there are machines and medications that can sustain the body even if the brain is "dead."

- Recent technology that allows for the transplant of many organs may motivate doctors to "pull the plug" on those who are brain dead. The "dead-donor rule," which prohibits causing death by organ removal, equates brain death with death.

- While there are tests that attempt to determine whether brain death has occurred, no hospital test can determine if there was a *yetzi'as haneshamah*.

- One should complete a healthcare proxy and EMES card, downloadable from Agudath Israel, when well and not under pressure, to ensure enforcement of your rights in end-of-life circumstances. One does not always have notice about the onset of circumstances necessitating these documents.

- One should also speak to family members about signing the necessary paperwork.

- A healthcare proxy is easy to complete. It does not require notarization and only needs to be signed before two witnesses. It can be copied and distributed to as many people as desired.

- Even when not faced with an emergency situation, one may not have the time or presence of mind to sign all documents with a clear head.

- Fighting what the documents state – or do not state – after the fact is very difficult.

- It is important to consult with a knowledgeable rabbi about end-of-life *halachos* when completing proxy forms and indicating one's wishes should one ever be in such a compromised state. There is a fine line between doing what is required by *halachah* to sustain a person and reducing their suffering, and there are specific *rabbanim* with expertise in this area.

- One should determine that the designated proxy clearly understands one's wishes.

- Be sure the patient's healthcare proxy is submitted correctly at any facility caring for the patient.

- The law in New Jersey allows one not to accept brain death as dead on religious grounds. In contrast, New York law allows staff to keep a person on machines for what they consider "reasonable accommodations."

- The family has the right to meet with a facility's ethics committee when there is a conflict between the patient's religious rights and the hospital's medical judgment regarding treatment. However, it is important to remain calm when doing so.

Eight Things You Can Do Now To Avoid Compounding Your Family's Pain Later

Rabbi Efrem Goldberg

D EATH IS A HIGHLY UNCOMFORTABLE AND awkward subject. As a result, most people do all they can to avoid the subject altogether. While we would prefer to see ourselves as living forever, the Torah instructs us that, in fact, reflecting on our mortality and being mindful of our transience are critical to living an inspired life and making the most of each day. Indeed, it is for this reason that King Solomon, the wisest of all men, encouraged us to prefer spending time in a house of mourning than spending time in a house of celebration.

Overcoming the taboo and talking about death are not only important to inspire how we live life, but are actually acts of love and devotion to those whom we will ultimately leave behind. A few years ago, a woman in our community died suddenly. She was never married and had no children, but I remembered that she had a brother. I went to her home and rifled through paperwork in an effort to find his information so that I could inform him of the terrible news. It took a significant amount of time to make contact with him and even longer to ascertain what arrangements she had made.

The more the deceased has planned, organized, and communicated his or her wishes, the less speculation, conflict, and compounded pain the bereaved will face at their time of loss and grief. Put simply, it is not

Rabbi Efrem Goldberg is the Senior Rabbi of the Boca Raton Synagogue (BRS) in Boca Raton, Florida. He has written numerous articles for Hamodia and Aish.com.

only negligent, but also unkind, not to have one's "matters in order," irrespective of how young or healthy he or she may presently be, or how uncomfortable it may be to think about and prepare for death.

None of us would ever intentionally cause or contribute to the pain or anguish of our family members. Yet failing to prepare likely will lead to complicating and, more likely, compounding the pain of our loved ones when we are gone.

For the sake of your family, please considering arranging the following as soon as possible:

1. **ICE** – Upon arriving at the scene of an accident or emergency, paramedics are trained to look on the patient's cell phone for an **ICE** – an In Case of Emergency entry that lists emergency contacts. Access to the right person and the right information can be the difference between life and death. Add an ICE entry to your cell phone phonebook immediately and consider downloading an ICE app that will allow access to your emergency contact(s) even when your phone is locked.

2. **Life Insurance** – Both Rav Moshe Feinstein (*Iggros Moshe Orach Chayim 2:111*) and Rav Ovadiah Yosef (*Yechaveh Da'at 3:85*) were asked if purchasing life insurance reflects a lack of faith and trust in G-d. They responded that as long as one remembers that it is G-d who empowered us with the wisdom to create life insurance and enabled us with this tool to protect our families, it is absolutely permitted and appropriate. They extend this endorsement to fire, theft, and car insurance as well. Nobody ever plans to be diagnosed with a terminal illness or to be the victim of a fatal accident. We cannot predict when our end will come, but we can plan so that the pain of our loss will not be compounded by financial instability, hardship and disaster.

3. **Disability Insurance** – Life insurance can help provide for one's family members if one dies, but what would happen if he or she suffered a debilitating injury or an incapacitating illness precluding the ability to work and provide an income? Disability insurance is only a luxury if it is never needed. We pray it will never be a necessity, but we would be foolish not to have it in case.

4. **Living Will and Health Care Proxy according to Jewish Law** – A myriad of complicated questions can arise in medical treatment, particularly at the end of life. This legal document empowers the

patient to determine in advance what choices he or she would prefer within the parameters of Jewish law and who is authorized to communicate those choices to medical professionals if the need arises. Moreover, rather than leaving wishes and desires ambiguous so that others are guessing and speculating, this document spells them out. Additionally, instead of conflict arising over how decisions are reached or which rabbinic authority should be consulted, the living will documents the decision-making process and sequence. The document can name a specific rabbi (or rabbis) or refer the decision to an organization, such as the Bioethics Committee of the Rabbinical Council of America. This is not a document reserved for the old or infirm. Every adult should have one on record, and it should be reviewed and updated every few years and as circumstances demand – and discussed with your spouse, children or relatives, so your wishes are clear.

5. **Will** – Don't leave loved ones guessing or fighting over how you want your assets divided. You work hard for your money, and it should be properly distributed among family, friends, and charities in a thoughtful, intentional and *halachic* manner. You can use your estate to leave not only a legacy for your family, but a legacy gift to the community, *shul* or schools that impacted your family. If you still have minor children, identify who will be responsible for them and ask their permission to stipulate such in your will. If you want to designate a specific piece of jewelry, art or memento to a particular person, specify that in your will or other document.

6. **Ethical Will** – When Ya'akov anticipated his demise, he called his family around his deathbed in order to give them each a blessing and charge them as a family. Throughout the millennia, prominent rabbis and leaders have recorded ethical wills communicating their values, vision, and passions to the next generation. Don't just leave children and grandchildren financial assets. Leave them your vision for who they can become and the most important values you hope they will pursue.

7. **Burial Arrangements** – Where do you want to be buried (i.e. locally or in Israel, in which cemetery, etc.)? Do you want a chapel service or a graveside service? Whom would you like to officiate? Does your family know that you want a Jewish burial according

to Jewish law and for them to sit a full *shivah* and to say Kaddish? Have you bought a plot and purchased a "pre-need" package with a funeral home, which is significantly less expensive that needing to buy it "at need?" Record your burial wishes in detail, including important biographical information that you would hope to be included in your eulogy, such as the major influences in your life and people and milestones that you were most grateful for or proud of. Are there particular relatives or friends or other people whom you would like to be invited to speak at your funeral?

8. **Organized File** – Perhaps most importantly, gather all of the above documentation and place it in a clearly designated place (paper and/or electronic) that your loved ones are aware of and have access to. Include your doctors, rabbi, and attorney and their contact information, your bank accounts, cemetery deed, safety deposit box (and location of keys), insurance information, financial advisors and brokers, inventory of assets and real estate, etc., so that nobody will be left guessing and searching for important information when it is needed. If you are one of those pack rats who hides money and jewelry in books or crevices around the house, tell someone where to look, so they do not get discarded with your other belongings or wind up with the next occupant of your house or apartment.

You may be reading this thinking it is excellent advice for someone else, for the elderly or the sick and infirm. But being responsible and planning appropriately is for every adult, every married person and certainly for every parent or grandparent. Don't only consider making all of these arrangements yourself, but plan to speak to your children and grandchildren about making such arrangements for themselves as well. Such preparations and arrangements are not taught in school. They rely on you to provide guidance and support in these areas. Not only is communicating these ideas to your children and grandchildren the right thing to do, but it is also in your interest, for their failure to plan will likely become your emergency.

May we all merit to live full and meaningful lives realizing great longevity. In the meantime, let's show our loved ones how much we care by making the proper preparations now, so they won't have to later.

This article is reprinted with permission from the author.

KEY POINTS:

- Reflecting on our mortality is critical to focusing on making the most of each day. There are also many practical ramifications in doing so.

- The more one has planned and communicated his wishes, the less unnecessary pain and confusion his family will need to deal with upon his death.

- Everyone, regardless of age and health status, should make time to do the following:

- Add an **ICE** (**In Case of Emergency**) entry to your cell-phone phonebook.

- Purchase a life insurance policy to provide for your family in case of tragedy.

- Purchase disability insurance to provide for your family should you suffer injury or debilitating illness.

- Sign a Living Will and health-care proxy that are in accordance with Jewish law. These documents should be reviewed and updated every few years and their contents discussed with family members.

- Write a legal will clearly defining how you want your assets divided. If you have minor children, specify who will be responsible for them.

- Write an ethical will, stating your most precious values, which you hope your family will perpetuate.

- Record your burial wishes in detail.

- Gather all of the abovementioned documents and place in a clearly designated location. Also include there a list of your doctors, rabbis, attorney, cemetery deed, bank accounts and any other financial information.

- Making these arrangements shows your loved ones you care about their future.

A Dry Run with Death

A PRACTICAL, 12-POINT CHECKLIST TO PREPARE FOR THE INEVITABLE

Mr. Martin I. Berger

(While we are not encouraging readers to follow the exact recommendations below per se, there are many important points that can be gleaned from this piece. -Ed.)

THE CALL CAME FROM MY MOTHER ON MY CELL phone. She was screaming into the phone that my dad had collapsed at the movies, and they were trying to revive him. By the time I got to the movie theater, eight paramedics were doing CPR on my seventy-two-year-old father, repeatedly shocking him with no response. One look at his lifeless body, and I knew it was over.

He had been in relatively good health. His heart surgery from twenty years prior had been a success, and it was only a week before his death that he started to get a bit tired when walking long distances. His doctor said it was probably congestive heart failure, but that people live another twenty years with that condition. He would schedule some tests, and everything would be fine. He never made it to the tests.

The hours after his death were a blur. Extreme shock at the loss of my best friend, the man I lived my life for, and the man I spent every Shabbos with for the last fifteen years of his life. This was not a tale of, "I wish I had told him I loved him." We said "I love you" to each other every day of our lives. But after the death, the pain of having to deal with "the details" started to engulf my life. I have three brothers, one living out of town and another who was on vacation in some remote mountains. Having to figure out the details of the burial and my father's desires for his funeral, and needing important information that was buried in a pile of his "papers," added immensely to my anguish and pain.

This was when I started to wish I had done a "dry run" of my father's death, at least once, before he passed away. At first thought, it might seem odd, even morbid, to prepare for death. But a little preparation is simply sensible. Yes, the discussion may be painful and sad. But everyone is going to die someday, and the last thing anyone wants to deal with is the details, such as which casket your parents did or did not pay for. Do a "dry run" now so that on the fateful day, you will be able to concentrate on the most important thing: mourning the loss of a loved one.

This idea applies to all nuclear families. If you are the parent of adult children, invite them to go through a dry run with you. And of course, spouses should be included, too.

12 Things to Prepare

1. Where do you want to be buried? Has the plot been paid for? If there are multiple plots in one area, in which one do you want to be buried? Draw an actual map of the plots, so there is no confusion as to the location of the grave.

   In making these decisions, it is also important to consult with a rabbi. There are many deep spiritual issues involved with the soul and burial, which can have eternal consequences, and it's best not to take chances in this area.

2. Have the funeral arrangements been paid for? (This is not the same as buying a plot.) Have arrangements been made for a *Chevrah Kaddisha*? Cemeteries are not the same things as funeral homes. The people you paid for a plot of land are not the same people who need to pick up the body and perform important functions like the *taharah*. These details will overwhelm anyone at a time when they are least able to handle it – unless it has been prearranged.

3. What kind of funeral service do you want? At a synagogue? In the chapel at the cemetery? Graveside? Would you like certain people to officiate or to speak?

4. Where are your bank accounts? What are the account numbers? Is there a safe deposit box? If so, who has the key? If not, then behind which wall/under which mattress is all the cash and jewels stored?

5. Where are your life insurance policies? If you don't have life insurance, buy it now. Proceeds from the policy can go toward mortgage payments, education funds, or anything that will prevent your demise from becoming an overwhelming financial burden for your family. When your family's financial future is secure, they can focus on piecing their lives back together.

6. Is there a Will? If so, who has the original? In many states, a photocopy does not suffice for probate and estate purposes.

   Where do you want your home and savings to go? Think not just of relatives, but of charities that you would like to support. Are there any personal possessions you would like to leave to particular individuals? Instead of trying to guess what your wishes might have been, your family can follow clear instructions that you have worked out after careful consideration.

   Many people avoid this because they feel that by having a Will, they are sealing a pact with death. Don't leave your family in chaos; give them the directives they need to honor your wishes properly, including division of property and assets and naming power of attorney, among others. If you die without a Will, state law determines how your assets will be divided – which may be very different from what you would have wanted. In addition, the court process can be lengthy and complex. Your estate may be tied up for a long time before your family can gain custody over your assets – causing them unnecessary hardship and heartache.

   Verbal instructions are entirely moot in a court of law. If you really want your wishes upheld, prepare a proper Will. Don't worry, you can always amend it at any time.

7. Are there any outstanding debts or loans? Sort these items out before death, so that everyone is prepared to address these potential liabilities when the time comes.

8. How are your financial accounts titled? Meet with a qualified accountant to set up trust funds, which will eliminate the need to put assets into probate. Take the time now to identify the assets in a potential estate and to create the appropriate trust into which these assets can pass.

9. Where are your most important papers stored? The more organized you are, the easier it will be for your family to sort

through the many challenges they face, whether it involves real estate, taxes, car loans, etc. Keep everything in a central place and make that location known.

10. What are your passwords? If you have website subscriptions, email accounts, etc., give your password(s) to your family so that they can deal with things as necessary.

11. If you were seriously ill, are there treatments you wouldn't want? These are terribly difficult decisions to leave to your family, and it is helpful to establish your wishes to guide them in the event that this ever proves necessary. As well, there are many serious issues in Jewish law (for example, some commonly-practiced terminations of life support are akin to murder). For all these issues, it is best to appoint a rabbi with a good knowledge of Jewish law to help mediate between family and physicians.

12. Whom would you like to notify? Write a list of the family members, friends or organizations that you would like notified upon your death.

Finally, buy a book on the Jewish laws of death and mourning. You are going to have many questions. What should I be doing from the time of death until the funeral? What are the laws and customs during the *shivah* (first seven days) and then during the first thirty days (*sheloshim*)? What are my social restrictions? Although it is easiest to consult your local rabbi for these answers, having a written guide close to your side is an incredible resource and source of comfort. You can print out two documents from www. JewishPathways.com. or buy one of these excellent books and put it on your bookshelf, just in case: *Mourning in Halachah* (ArtScroll) or *The Jewish Way in Death and Mourning* by Maurice Lamm. [*Ed. Note: Visit www.ChevrahLomdeiMishnah.org for some excellent materials, including Burial Prayers, Concise Laws of Shivah and To Comfort and Be Comforted.*]

Although this list is not exhaustive, it's a good start. Take the time to do a dry run. Speak to your close family members. Become educated and face the inevitable. Thank G-d, my father's passing has only managed to bring my brothers and me even closer than we were before. Unfortunately, however, I know too many people who allow longstanding feuds to fester without anyone taking the first step to rectify the differences. Make peace now. Put to rest your family squabbles so that everyone can enjoy that elusive "closure." In the end, you only get one chance.

Whether the passing is sudden or prolonged, nothing can prepare you for the loss of a loved one. It is painful. It is sad. But if you take some time now and address these issues, your family will have the opportunity to mourn properly at the time of their most profound loss.

With thanks to Roger Darlington, Pauline Go, Fine-Tuned Finances, ehow.com, and advocis.ca.

This article is reprinted with permission from Aish.com.

KEY POINTS:

- While it might be uncomfortable, taking the time to discuss details relevant after your death can save your family much aggravation.

- Topics to be discussed include burial wishes; funeral arrangements; financial information; life insurance; writing a will and sharing the whereabouts of the original copy; location of important papers; disclosure of passwords; treatments to be avoided should you become ill and designation of a rabbi to mediate between doctors and family members.

- Buy a book on the Jewish laws of death and mourning and keep it on your shelf.

- Make peace with family members now.

- Addressing this topic today will allow your family to mourn properly when the time comes.

Bring Out the Best

Rabbi Mordechai Rhine

O NE OF THE KEY WAYS IN WHICH CAREGIVERS can proactively assist a dying patient is by helping them to take action while they are capable of doing so and to achieve clarity about who they are and what message they wish to leave over. *Halachah* recognizes the delicate nature of end-of-life situations. On one hand, it is a great merit to recite *viduy* (confession and its related prayers) before passing. In addition, the opportunity to share an ethical will and final message with one's loved ones is extremely valuable. At the same time, great caution must be exercised lest such discussions (which often take place only during end-of-life situations) dishearten the sick person (see *Yoreh Dei'ah* 338: end of 1). Thus, because we are afraid of disheartening a person and damaging their fragile health, they lose out on maximizing the final days of life.

One suggestion to get around this concern is that a person should be guided to say the *viduy* prayer whenever confronting a significant medical situation. Thus, a friend of mine shared with me that his father recited the *viduy* prayer five or six times before his actual passing, as he recited it before each significant surgery and when he was transferred to critical care. The basic prayer states, "I acknowledge before You, G-d, that my health is in Your hands. May it be Your will to heal me completely, and in the merit of my *viduy*, please do so. When I die, may my passing be an atonement on all sins that I have committed, and grant me a portion in the World to Come" (based on *Yoreh Dei'ah* 338:1, 2).

[*Ed. Note: For a more in-depth discussion on the topic of viduy, see A Ticket to Olam Haba, on page 207 of this volume.*]

Rabbi Mordechai Rhine is the rav of Southeast Hebrew Congregation-Knesset Yehoshua in White Oak, MD. He also is the Director of TEACH613, which promotes Torah and mitzvah education through classes and virtual media. Rabbi Rhine provides personalized speed-coaching on a variety of mitzvah and relationship topics. He can be reached at RMRhine@teach613.org.

A caregiver can also encourage a patient who is still capable to write an ethical will. This can be two to three paragraphs addressed to family and friends regarding what a person feels is memorable about his (or her) life, how he wants to be remembered, and what advice he would like to share. Besides the value of leaving behind a written communication, the experience of composing such a message helps a person clarify what he or she does consider noteworthy and which life experiences are worth sharing with loved ones.

On a positive note, the caregiver can encourage a patient to write precisely because it must be written while a person is well and can do so. Doing so does not involve discussion about sin or shortcomings. Rather it is simply a chance to "bring out the best" of what a person feels is important, as he reflects on what he would like his legacy in this world to be.

One interesting end-of-life option involves a visit with a musician who is trained in basic counseling. The musician interviews the patient to learn what kind of music he enjoys, as well as what values or memorable experiences he considers noteworthy to be included in a song. Then, together, they co-author a song of music and lyrics which they practice and then record, so that the patient can listen to it and find comfort during the challenging months ahead. A side benefit to this process is that thinking and reflecting while authoring the song can be most valuable to a person with health challenges who wishes to "sort things out."

A caregiver is uniquely positioned to help the patient through his challenge by assisting him in "bringing out his best" and expressing it. This will hopefully enable the patient to achieve personal clarity and to use his final days in the most productive way possible.

KEY POINTS:

- One of the most valuable ways to assist a dying patient is to help them maximize their final days and bring out the best elements of the lives they have lived.

- To avoid discouraging the patient by suggesting recital of *viduy*, one can instead guide the ill person to recite *viduy* whenever confronting a significant medical situation.

- Caregivers can encourage the patient to write an ethical will while he is still able. This is valuable not only for the patient's family, but is also a way for the patient to crystalize the message he most wants to relay to his loved ones.

- A musician trained in counseling can co-author a song with the ill person, which can provide comfort to that person in the days or months ahead. This can also help the patient clarify his values and most memorable life experiences.

Writing an Ethical Will

Libi Astaire

PERHAPS YOU'VE THOUGHT OF WRITING A MEMOIR or even started one. But no sooner do you free up an hour or two than you find that your finger has mysteriously gotten stuck on your keyboard's procrastination key. Is there another way to pass your hard-earned wisdom and cherished values to your children and grandchildren? The solution could be to write an ethical will, which was our ancestors' ego-document of choice for centuries. The beauty of the ethical will is that there are no rules. It can be long or short. It can cover a broad range of topics, or it can focus on just a few. It can include a short biography of the writer, or it can jump right into the matters that are near and dear to the author's heart. Still, there is that scary blank screen staring at you, so how do you get started?

A tried-and-true technique is to ask yourself questions, such as: what important things have I learned in my life? What are the character traits that I most admire? Is there a particular charitable cause or organization that I've dedicated significant amounts of time to, which I hope my children will continue to support? You can also think about techniques you've developed to overcome obstacles, perhaps in learning, or in guarding your temper, which you would like to share with your descendants. Or perhaps you have some good advice for how to maintain *shalom bayis* or make Shabbos meaningful for the entire family. Once you get started, the ideas will probably start to flow without any more prodding. But remember: when you've finished the document, be sure to keep it in a place where it will be easily found. Some people attach a copy to their legal will, so that it can be read at the appropriate time.

Libi Astaire is the author of the award-winning Jewish Regency Mystery Series; Terra Incognita, a novel about the crypto-Jews of Spain; and The Banished Heart, a novel about Shakespeare's writing of The Merchant of Venice, as well as numerous history-related articles in Mishpacha/Family First magazine. She lives in Jerusalem, Israel.

Reprinted with permission from Mishpacha/Family First magazine, where this article originally appeared.

Reprinted from To Fill The Sky with Stars with permission from Menucha Publishers.

KEY POINTS:

- There are no rules about writing an ethical will – it can be long or short, broad-ranging or very focused.

- Helpful questions to get you started: What important things have I learned in life? What character traits do I admire? Is there a cause about which I feel strongly/have dedicated significant time?

- Consider sharing helpful advice or techniques for overcoming obstacles.

- Keep your finished document somewhere where it will be easily found, such as attached to your legal will.

CHAPTER V

The Value of Life: End-of-Life Challenges

Life-And-Death Decisions

AN INTERVIEW WITH RABBI ELCHONON ZOHN,
DIRECTOR OF THE NATIONAL ASSOCIATION OF
CHEVRA KADISHA

Rabbi Gavriel Horan

W HAT BEGAN AS A REGULAR FRIDAY NIGHT became a nightmare when Mr. Green, eighty-three, fell down in the street on his way to *shul*. By the time Hatzolah arrived, he had gone into cardiac arrest, and by the time he was stabilized, he had already sustained serious brain damage. Based on the severity of the damage, the doctors advised the family that he was brain-dead, suggested they sign a DNR (**D**o **N**ot **R**esuscitate) and a DNI (**D**o **N**ot **I**ntubate) order and discussed the possibility of removing him from the respirator.

The family immediately consulted with a *rav*. They spoke with Rabbi Elchonon Zohn, the director of the National Association of Chevra Kadisha (NASCK), who advised them to wait a little while before making any decisions.

After a few days Mr. Green started to show signs of improvement. Despite the doctors' grim prognosis, after three months, he was back home. Although he needed assistance, he *davened* three times every day and was blessed to spend another year and a half with his beloved family, enjoying tremendous *simchas hachayim*. If the Greens had listened to the doctors, Mr. Green might never have woken up.

Rabbi Gavriel Horan spent five years working for Aish HaTorah on college campuses in New York. He currently lives in Baltimore, MD, where he continues to work as an outreach rabbi, therapist, life coach, journalist and grant writer.

ALL ACROSS THE UNITED STATES AND AROUND THE world, the sanctity of life is being challenged by the medical

Challenge to the Sanctity of Life

community's changing view of life and death. Now more than ever before, doctors and health-insurance companies are reluctant to administer medical care in a growing number of cases, specifically those involving elderly or comatose patients. An example of this trend is a concept discussed at a recent conference for managed health-care plans known as age-based health-care rationing, which recommends limited use of medical intervention for elderly patients.

Family members are often encouraged to choose not to resuscitate their loved ones on the grounds that it will only "prolong their suffering." However, stories abound of sudden recoveries occurring just days after doctors declared there was no hope, as in the case of Mr. Green. As the Gemara tells us (*Berachos 10a*), "Even if the sharp sword rests on your neck, don't give up [anticipating Hashem's] compassion."

Rabbi Zohn has been the head of the Chevra Kadisha of Queens and Long Island since 1981 and founded NASCK in 1996. As director of both organizations, he is involved in the fight against unnecessary autopsies and cremation in America. Although he has spent much of his life working to preserve the honor of the dead, he recently took up the reins of a new campaign to protect the living.

"The average Jew stands the chance of being in a situation where the end-of-life decisions that will be made for him by his family and his doctors will be contrary to *halachah*," Rabbi Zohn explained. "In the United States, the law is that a person has a right as a patient to demand treatment. Patient autonomy protects a patient's rights; however, if he is unable to make these requests for himself, the family representing him really has zero legal standing. If one cannot speak for himself, the doctors can legally do – or not do – whatever they believe is 'medically indicated.'"

Rabbi Zohn pointed out that *Forbes* magazine, a popular American business journal, recently published an article addressing the fact that estate planning is not only about money; it also has to do with medical directives. In an emergency, it is imperative that each individual protect his or her right to choose a course of action that is in accordance with his wishes. The article recommended that it be a "right of passage" for all eighteen-year-olds to designate a health-care proxy, since accidents are the major cause of death among eighteen to twenty-five-year-olds and parents have no power to make decisions for them if they are not designated as proxies.

For Jews, the problem is that the preferred decision of health-care professionals is frequently in direct contrast to Torah values – and if proper precautions are not taken before it's too late, there is often little that can be done to fight it.

"We Jews have an added incentive to maintain control over the decision-making process. We don't only believe that pulling the plug is wrong, but it is also a possible issue of *pikuach nefesh* [a life-and-death decision] and *retzichah d'Oraisa* [murder according to Torah law], and you should voice that opinion to someone who has the legal authority to enforce it in the case of a medical emergency," Rabbi Zohn emphasized.

"A health-care proxy assumes the power to speak on your behalf with all the rights that you yourself possess. Members of the *frum* community must go a step further to direct their representative to consult with the rabbi of their choice should a life-and-death *shailah* arise."

THE SOLUTION, ACCORDING TO RABBI ZOHN, IS THE EMES wallet card. [*Ed. Note: See sample EMES card on page 219.*]

An Urgent Campaign EMES is an acronym for the Emergency Medical Education and Sign-Up campaign, which was created with the guidance of Agudath Israel's legal staff and advances the goals of Chayim Aruchim, a project of Agudath Israel that encourages the signing of an Agudath Israel Advanced Medical Directive. The EMES card is small and can be attached directly to your driver's license or ID card with a special sleeve that clearly displays your end-of-life wishes in case of an emergency. The most important component is your designation of a health-care proxy and the completion of a living will. A health-care proxy specifies the name(s) of the agent(s) who are to be given legal power to carry out your wishes in making emergency medical decisions of life-and-death significance.

A living will, also known as a MOLST or POLST form (**M**edical or **P**hysician **O**rders for **L**ife-**S**ustaining Treatment), specifies the medical directives of your choice in a variety of situations for the health-care proxy or others to follow. The generic living-will form contains numerous scenarios with possible actions that need to be confirmed or denied; for example, "If I am in a vegetative state, I do/ don't want to be resuscitated."

Although in many cases the DNR option is against *halachah*, each situation must be examined carefully by a qualified rabbinical authority. The *halachah* is rarely black and white, and it is necessary to designate a knowledgeable rabbi to facilitate these decisions should they be necessary.

Therefore, Agudath Israel and the Rabbinical Council of America have developed their own living-will form, known as a Halachic Living Will, which includes a health-care proxy and a living will. The difference is that this living will does not include specific situations; instead it indicates the name of the rabbi who should be consulted if the proxy has any questions that are *halachic* in nature. Agudath Israel of America and the Orthodox Union have arranged, free of charge, for the registration of the living will with the U.S. Living Will Registry.

WHEN AN ELDERLY *FRUM* WOMAN WAS IN THE LAST stages of cancer, the doctors wanted her to sign a DNR. She was at

To Do or Not to Do
peace with herself and had accepted the decree that her life was nearing its end. She didn't want to put her family through the trauma of keeping her alive in a vegetative state, and she was physically and emotionally drained by years of invasive treatment. She asked that she be required to undergo only the minimal amount of intervention permitted by *halachah*. In the end, the *rabbanim* consulted concurred that she did not have an obligation to request resuscitation if she didn't want it.

On the other hand, there are countless stories of people who are instructed to forgo treatments such as chemotherapy, dialysis, or putting in a PEG or feeding tube, or who are urged to "pull the plug" on a sick family member, only to find that the patient recovers and goes on to live many years in good health. Following are two examples of many:

An elderly *frum* man in his eighties suffered from kidney failure, and the hospital refused to put him on dialysis, claiming that such treatment was better reserved for younger patients. The family fought the decision and won, and the man went on to live several more happy and relatively healthy years.

Another elderly woman contracted pneumonia. She was admitted to the hospital and treated. A few weeks after she was released, she came down with it again, and the same thing happened a third time. At that point her doctor called the family together and informed them that her heart had stopped functioning properly and that she was fighting a losing battle. "This is cruel treatment," he said. "Let her die in peace, without all this forceful intervention."

The family went to a *rav*, who told them that they had an obligation to continue to treat the woman's pneumonia. They went to another doctor for a second opinion; he decided to run a few tests and discovered that the pneumonia had nothing to do with her "failing" heart. Instead it turned out that she was swallowing her food poorly due to a problem with her swallowing reflex, as a result of which food was entering her windpipe and lungs, causing infection to develop. He recommended occupational therapy to teach her to swallow properly, and she lived in good health for another four years.

Comfort Vs. Challenge

"HOSPITALS TODAY ARE MOVING IN A DIRECTION WHERE they are discouraging people from requesting heroic interventions," Rabbi Zohn explained. According to him, the primary reason for this is that intensive care is extremely expensive and the insurance companies don't want to pay for it.

Another reason is that hospitals often receive grants and ratings based on the number of fatalities relative to the number of patients they treat. They therefore want to avoid fatalities at all costs.

This means that it is better for hospitals to encourage people to turn to hospices, where patients are given medication to ease their pain and discomfort but are not treated for their condition. In many cases, hospices refuse to give hydration or nutrition to patients in the end stages of life, essentially starving them to death in order to let them die "with dignity." According to almost all *halachic* opinions, however, this translates into nothing short of murder.

"In today's world, this is somewhat understandable," Rabbi Zohn continued. "People equate life with comfort. If it isn't comfortable, why stay alive? As *frum* Jews, we have a completely opposite view. Life isn't about comfort; it's about work and growth. *L'fum tza'ara agra*

– the reward is according to the *dis*comfort! According to the Torah, every second of life is valuable, and we have an obligation to protect it at all costs within the context of *halachah*."

To prove this last point, he quotes an interesting interpretation of Harav Shlomo Zalman Auerbach, *zt"l*, cited in the *sefer Nishmas Avraham* by Dr. Abraham S. Abraham, regarding the *Asarah Harugei Malchus*, whose story is part of the *tefillah* on Tishah B'Av and Yom Kippur. After the decapitation of Rabi Shimon ben Gamliel, Rabi Yishmael Kohen Gadol picked up the severed head and wept. Rav Shlomo Zalman was asked how Rabi Yishmael could do this since he was a *kohen*, and it is forbidden for a *kohen* to become ritually impure. His answer was that as a condemned prisoner, Rabi Yishmael couldn't so much as move a limb without asking permission from the Roman authorities. Going through the process of asking the prison guards to consider his strange and morbid request bought him another few minutes of life. Even a few moments of life on Death Row are precious, and overriding the *issur* of becoming impure complies with the Torah dictum "*v'chai bahem*."

ANOTHER CRUCIAL ISSUE IS THAT OF AUTOPSIES. THE medical examiner often requires a definitive cause of death, even in cases where there is a very probable cause.

Protecting the Departed

For example, in the instance of a car accident resulting in a fatality, authorities may want to know if the death was a direct result of the accident or whether it was caused by a heart attack or some other illness that may have caused the driver to lose control. There could be differences in the insurance policy for payment based on whether it was an accidental or natural death. Furthermore, they may want to identify disease for genetic purposes. So in many cases, autopsies are performed, even though the cause of death is natural and obvious.

However, unless an autopsy is needed to help solve a suspected murder case or to prevent a potential epidemic, it is often completely unnecessary. Many states do not accommodate a family's religious objection to an autopsy, and some will accommodate only when there is a signed objection made by the decedent himself – and even this is insufficient in certain states that currently lack the legislation to defend a person's right to avoid an autopsy.

"Having a signed card will assist us if it is necessary to fight against state legal authorities, and the buzz of this campaign may encourage legislators to consider passing new laws to uphold freedom of choice in this issue throughout the country," Rabbi Zohn said. "Furthermore, at the present time, although organ donations are not the default mode in the United States, there are suggestions to make them such, as they are in Europe."

Another pressing issue that often comes up is cremation. All too often Rabbi Zohn receives calls from *frum* people, often *ba'alei teshuvah*, who need help fighting a non-*frum* relative's request to be cremated. Rabbi Zohn often asks why the subject wasn't discussed when the departed was still alive, and the answer is almost always that they didn't know how to raise the subject.

Rabbi Zohn explained that the EMES cards open the door to discussing last wishes with non-*frum* relatives, friends, or co-workers. He pointed out that there are even times when the *niftar* requests burial, but the immediate family prefers to save money by cremating the body. "If an agent isn't appointed," he said, "one's last wishes are usually not binding unless the case goes to court. The EMES card legally designates that proxy. This is the only way to ensure that the *halachah* is upheld in life and in death."

NASCK is encouraging *shuls* and communities to address these issues in public lectures or events culminating in a sign-up drive, with all the forms and cards provided by volunteers who can answer questions so participants can confidently sign the cards once they are filled in. Forms and instructions for how to register a halachic living will with the U.S. Living Will Registry, free of charge, are also available online.

Rabbi Zohn hopes that the successful implementation of this campaign will be a significant step forward in the religious community's efforts to encourage greater adherence to the *halachos* of *pikuach nefesh* and *kevurah k'halachah* among our observant brethren and all of *Klal Yisrael*.

To download all the necessary forms, to register and for more information, please contact NASCK at (718) 847-6280 or (888) 243-8721, or email info@nasck.org.

This article originally appeared in Hamodia and is reprinted with that publication's permission and that of the author.

KEY POINTS:

- Doctors and insurance companies are increasingly reluctant to administer healthcare to a growing number of patients, particularly those who are elderly or comatose.

- In many cases in which families were instructed to forego treatment for their loved one, the patient went on to recover and/or live a productive life.

- Hospitals today are increasingly discouraging people from requesting heroic interventions, mainly due to the high-cost of care.

- Hospitals encourage failing patients to transfer to hospice, where the focus is on managing pain, as opposed to treating the condition. They may also withhold nutrition and hydration to hasten death.

- If a patient in the United States cannot speak for himself, the doctors can legally do – or not do – whatever they believe is "medically indicated," no matter the family's wishes.

- Decisions of healthcare professionals are frequently in contrast to Torah values, and if proper precautions are not taken, there is little that can be done to legally fight such decisions.

- A healthcare proxy specifies the name(s) of the agent(s) given legal power to make emergency medical decisions on your behalf.

- A living will specifies the medical directions of one's choice in a variety of situations. The halachic living will does not include specific situations and instead indicates the name of a rabbi to be consulted if the proxy should have any *halachic* questions.

- A most effective precautionary measure is to sign the EMES (Emergency Medical Education and Sign Up) wallet card, which can be attached to your driver's license or id card for easy reference in case of emergency. This card includes the designation of a health-care proxy and the completion of a halachic living will.

- Having a signed card indicating one's opposition to autopsy and organ donation is also important, should it be necessary to fight state legal authorities regarding these areas.

- Suggesting that loved ones sign the EMES card can be a helpful way of opening the door to discussing their last wishes and why it is so important to choose burial over cremation.

- EMES cards and instructions for how to register a halachic living will with the US Living Will Registry, free of charge, are available online.

- The world's view is that life should be comfortable. The Jewish view is that life is about work and growth and every second of life is valuable.

Religion Saved The Athiest Patient

Rabbi Moshe Taub

ITHOUT QUESTION, THE MOST SERIOUS situations that *rabbanim* and their membership face, and this comes up quite often, are end-of-life issues. On many levels, this is an intensely challenging yet contentious topic. The questions are myriad; when/if to sign a DNR; how to write a healthcare proxy; estate planning; counseling.

IT IS MY HOPE THAT THE BASIC EDUCATION SUPPLIED here will be an effective motivator for people to speak to their

Ask the Questions Now

rabbanim to better prepare for these possible unfortunate situations. All too often, families are irrevocably split due to these matters not being addressed before a tragedy strikes. Understandably, examining *halachic* and *hashkafic* principles mustn't be delayed to the least opportune time. It therefore behooves each and every one of us, *l'ma'an haShalom* and *l'ma'an halachah*, to reflect on these issues with our personal *moreh hora'ah*.

While I am writing in the role of a rabbi, my experience in these matters is beyond merely the professional, as I have, sadly, spent much time in the ICU with family members as well.

A few years ago, a dear member of our *shul* was diagnosed with his final illness. He fought valiantly. In his final days, although somewhat delirious, he was conscious and constantly complaining of his dry throat. The family was concerned about the efficacy and safety of the ice chips that were being used as a source of relief. Approaching the doctor on call, they asked if there was perhaps a better way to relieve

---

Rabbi Moshe Taub served as the rav of the Young Israel of Greater Buffalo and the rav hamachshir in Boutique Kosher certifiers from 2003 to 2015. He is now the rav of the Young Israel of Holliswood, Queens and teaches in a number of schools and organizations in the New York area.

the patient's discomfort, like an IV, which would eliminate, or at least assuage, his dehydration. The doctor was shocked – shocked! – that this family would seek to sustain the patient in *any* way. She pushed for a complete termination of all nourishment, and more, an increase in morphine to "alleviate the pain." *Halachically*, virtually all major *poskim* agree that nourishment must always *be given* to all patients at all times[1]. In addition, no *posek* would allow a termination of relief when the patient is asking for it. As for the morphine, although euthanasia is illegal in the state of NY, morphine is often used as a ploy, as in large doses it can suppress the respiratory system, leading to death. The family was horrified. They promptly called me to come down to the hospital and speak to the doctor. Now, admittedly, I am not a trained physician, and it's indeed beyond my breadth of knowledge to discuss *how* to end/extend lives, yet it always amazes me how sure some doctors are of their personal view regarding end-of-life issues. This doctor, bluntly, made it clear that as a rabbi my view – while perhaps holding sway over the family – was not relevant to her medical opinion. I asked (and I paraphrase), "Your *medical* opinion? While reasonable people could argue about these issues, they are *ethical* ones and not based solely on science, as there is no scientific data, as of yet, that has conclusively closed this debate. To stop all nourishment in one's final days or when a person is first diagnosed with a terminal illness, or to allow for pain or discomfort – whether it is a minute before the death of a patient or for a healthy child – is not an execution of scientific knowledge, per se, but rather, a reflection of a personal view seen through the prism of a serious debate that is happening across all religions and secular ethicists." She "allowed" us to give him an IV for three days only (he passed away the next day).[2]

The July 21, 2006 issue of *The Wall Street Journal* ran a column entitled, *"How Faith Saved the Atheist."* In this column, the writer tells the story of how when her father lay dying in a NY hospital, every

---

1   For instance, see Rabbi Shlomo Zalman Auerbach in Minchas Shlomo 91:24; Rabbi Moshe Feinstein in Iggros Moshe, Choshen Mishpat II:74:3.

2   This story is not unique. Indeed, the consensus among modern secular ethicists is to remove nutrition and oxygen in such cases. See Encyclopedia Halchtit Repho'it (Dr. Steinberg) vol. 4, page 438, ff 484, for sources for this secular consensus. See also English translation of that work (3 volumes, Feldheim) page 1085, ff 299.

doctor sought to convince them to let him "die with dignity" and not to seek to extend his time further. The writer, an unaffiliated Jew, came up with a ruse: she told the doctors that her father was an Orthodox Jew (he was not) and this finally caused, in her words, "an invisible fence" to go up around their family. The writer remarks: *"Though my father was born to an Orthodox Jewish family, he is an avowed atheist who long ago had rejected his parents' ways. As I sat in the ICU, blips on the various screens the only proof that my father was alive, the irony struck me: my father, who had long ago rejected Orthodox Judaism, was now under its protection."*

Of course, the situation above of a dismissive doctor can be reversed; there are times when a *rav* might *pasken* that *no* further medical treatment be started for the patient, while the doctor might disagree. This can be awfully uncomfortable, as when a doctor once asked me, "How can a 'Jewish rabbi' rule like this?"

IN ADDITION TO THE INNUMERABLE *HALACHIC* concerns involved in end-of-life issues, it is critical to be able to offer

The Value of an Objective View

objective and calm views when adjudicating such profound decisions. One's doctor, while dedicated and caring, cannot honestly claim that they can be completely objective as they are under pressure for open beds in the ICU and in caring for the patient as they slowly pass. This subconscious subjectivity can be true even regarding the patient's family. To illustrate, I am sometimes asked the following painful question; "Can we *daven* that Hashem take the *neshamah* of our loved one, being that he is suffering terribly from a terminal disease?" Indeed the *Tzitz Eliezer*[3] and others write extensively on this topic. After marshaling many sources allowing for such *tefillos*, many authorities end by saying that while one can argue for the allowance of a prayer for *netilas neshamah*, those taking care of the patient – especially the immediate family – cannot do so, for although they are dedicated and have much love for the patient, they are not completely objective and could benefit emotionally, especially at this stage, with

---

3   18:48:5, also 5: Ramat Rachel:5. See also Iggros Moshe Choshen Mishpat II:73:1 and 74:4. See also Chavatzeles HaSharon, Parshas Vayeira.

the patient's demise[4]. The point to infer from this is simple: we all need an objective voice when we are so emotionally attached and worn.

FOR THE ABOVE REASONS, IT WOULD BE HIGHLY advantageous to speak to a competent *halachic* authority and

Healthcare Proxy and Living Will

knowledgeable lawyer to draw up two important documents. One is called a healthcare proxy. In this document, one names an individual who would have the power over all medical decisions should one become incapacitated. The living will picks up where the healthcare proxy leaves off by explaining about specific directives to the proxy, such as to which *rabbanim* to ask *shailos* (more than one should be offered, as not always is a *rav* accessible). Due to the controversial issues involved, it should not come as a surprise that there is significant debate among *rabbanim* regarding these issues, specifically relating to the 1968 Harvard criteria of "brain death." Although a significant number of modern secular ethicists concur with these findings – thereby allowing for all major organ transplants such as that of the heart, liver, etc. – a vast majority of the *poskim* strongly oppose the idea that cessation of brain activity is the catalyst for death (Rabbis Elyashiv, Feinstein, Auerbach, Waldenberg, *inter alia*.). We must be aware of this discussion so as to know how to choose which rabbi we wish to name in the living will.

Agudath Israel has such forms available for download, as do many other organizations.

In 1772 the Duke of Mecklenburg demanded that all bodies remain unburied for three days to assure that death actually took place. The *maskilim* supported this decree, while the *Chasam Sofer*[5] and major *poskim* were opposed, demanding that we rely on *halachah* and *mesorah* and not fear or personal whims.

While many believe that *halachah* is always stringent when it comes to these issues, the truth is that the only concern in *hashkofas haTorah* is for *Toras Emes* to be fulfilled, whether that manifests as a leniency or stringency.

Reprinted with permission from Ami Magazine and that of the author.

---

4   See *Pachad Yitzchak Aruch*, *"goses,"* for a nusach tefillah for the demise of the terminally ill, r"l.

5   *Y.D. 338*

KEY POINTS:

- One should prioritize speaking to a knowledgeable *rav* to gain *halachic* and *hashkafic* understanding of end-of-life issues before tragedy strikes.

- It is critical to offer objective and calm views when discussing with doctors and family member matters regarding end-of-life care.

- Not only is it difficult for doctors to remain objective regarding the care of a terminally ill patient, but even family members might find themselves swayed by emotional or personal concerns.

- The abovementioned reality underscores the importance of drawing up a healthcare proxy and living will, with the guidance of a competent *halachic* authority and lawyer.

- A healthcare proxy identifies the agent who will have power over all medical decisions, should one become incapacitated.

- A living will picks up where the healthcare proxy leaves off, delineating to the proxy specific directives regarding medical care, including which *rabbanim* to consult when *shailos* arise.

- Both the healthcare proxy and living will are available online from Agudath Israel, as well as other organizations.

Life Itself

Rabbi Avi Shafran

IN THE NETHERLANDS, A FIFTEEN-YEAR-OLD NEEDS parental consent to enlist a doctor's help in killing herself. If she waits until she's sixteen, although she needs to "involve" her parents in her decision, she need not receive their approval. Nor need she be suffering any terminal medical condition; emotional pain is sufficient legal justification to assist in her suicide.

Legal euthanasia in The Netherlands is defined as "active termination of life on request." It does not include what is known as "terminal sedation" – the administering of morphine in quantities that relieve pain but also hasten death.

But if a Dutch doctor chooses to "terminally sedate" patients in pain without the consent of the patient or family members, "it doesn't need to be reported," according to Rob Jonquiere, a physician who heads a pro-euthanasia group, "Right to Die – Netherlands." "We don't know," he admits, "how many doctors do that."

However many there may be, though, they are at least subtly encouraged in performing such "mercy killings" by the fact that the law in their country permits assisted suicide. "Terminal sedation" may not have similar legal sanction at present, but its goal, to be sure, is the same as the goal of assisted suicide: freeing people from pain, forever.

"Mak[ing] people happy" was how Canadian-born Dutch nurse, Lucy de Berk, referred in her diary to an unspecified secret she wrote she would take with her to the grave. She was convicted last March of murdering three terminally ill children and an elderly woman at two hospitals in The Hague.

We don't yet know what Charles Cullen's motivation may have been in having ended, as he has claimed, the lives of up to 40 patients

---

Rabbi Avi Shafran has been the director of public affairs and spokesman for Agudath Israel of America since 1994. He writes widely for Jewish media and is the author of five books.

in New Jersey and Pennsylvania hospitals over the course of his own career as a nurse. But it is certainly conceivable that he too felt he was doing a good deed in helping others in distress shuffle off this mortal coil.

Such sentiments, if not their immoral application, are easy to empathize with; most of us would readily act upon them ourselves for livestock or pets *in terminus*. At the same time, though, we maintain a deep commitment to something that our Torah has clearly and resolutely taught for thousands of years: human life is different.

Suicide is regarded by *halachah* as an *aveirah*, and "pulling the plug" of a patient on life-support machinery, even where natural death is imminent, is considered the taking of a life. All the Torah's laws, with the exception only of the three cardinal ones (idolatry, immorality and murder), are put aside when life – even for a limited period – is in the balance.

Whence Judaism's exquisite valuation of even momentary human life? A likely reason lies in a recognition pondered by far too few and far too infrequently.

It is not surprising that the terminally ill (or, as in Dutch law, even the gravely despondent) are seen in our times as prime beneficiaries of their own deaths. Ours is a culture, after all, where human worth is often measured by intellectual prowess or mercantile skills – even by things like youth or physical beauty, or the capacity to convincingly impersonate a real or fictional character, or to strongly and accurately hit, kick or throw a ball.

The too-little-pondered recognition is that the true value of human beings lies elsewhere entirely, in men and women's potential to do good things – to prepare, in fact, for an existence beyond the one we know. When that idea – self-evident to some, challenging to others – is internalized, a very different sensibility emerges.

And among the perceptions it affords is that there is immeasurable value in human life itself – even in its minutes and seconds, and even when it is fettered by infirmity, immobility, or depression.

Basketball or dancing may no longer be options in the confines of a hospital bed, and even tending to one's most basic physical needs may be impossible without help. But are acts of sheer will – like *mechilah, teshuvah, emunah, hachlatah, ahavas Hashem, ahavas haberiyos* or *tefillah* – any harder to accomplish, or any less meaningful? Are they compromised in any way by tangles of tubes and monitors?

Not even consciousness, at least as medically defined, need hinder what humanly matters most. Contemporary science chooses to take electronic brain activity as evidence of being meaningfully conscious, of the ability to think and choose, and then proceeds to conclude that in the absence of such evidence, those abilities must no longer exist – without a thought (at least a conscious one) of the immense tautology thereby embraced.

We do not know, cannot know, when a human being is truly incapacitated – when his or her *neshamah* has been released. Only when a heart has stopped beating can we be certain that life in its truest sense has ended. And so hastening or abetting the death of even a physically or emotionally compromised human being is no less an ending of meaningful life than gunning down a healthy, happy one.

The attitude regarding human life codified in the Netherlands today is one toward which much of contemporary Western culture, unfortunately, is slouching. It is spoken of by sophisticates as "progressive," and indeed represents a progression of sorts, away from the Torah that is the bedrock of what are called morality and ethics. The degree to which the world manages to check that progression will be the degree to which it demonstrates that it truly understands what it means to be human.

This article is reprinted from Agudath Israel archives, with permission from the author.

KEY POINTS:

- Legal euthanasia in the Netherlands is defined as "the active termination of life on request." This does not include "terminal sedation," the administering of morphine in quantities that ease pain **and hasten death**. Terminal sedation can be administered in that country without the consent of a parent or family member.

- In contrast to today's culture where human worth is measured by external abilities, Torah Jews measure human worth by one's potential to do good things and prepare for a future, eternal existence. The byproduct of this perception is an immeasurable value for human life, even when that life is severely limited in some way.

- There are many meaningful activities that can still be accomplished by one who is very ill, i.e., *emunah, ahavas Hashem, ahavas haberiyos, tefillah.*

- Even a person who is unconscious is still accomplishing, so long as his *neshamah* is within him.

- Hastening death even of someone who seems very compromised physically and emotionally is tantamount to murder.

Be Prepared – A Guide to End of Life Circumstances

Rabbi Naftali Katz

THE CALL FOR ASSISTANCE CAME TO ME FROM the caregiver of a Jewish man who was nearing the end of his life. Making a determination that his patient was not going to live much longer, the doctor decided that there was no point in prolonging the life of the patient by providing him with nutrition or hydration. After obtaining the specifics of the case, I explained to the doctor in a respectful manner our perspective on the value of every moment of human life and asked that he continue providing the patient with proper nutrition in any way possible. The doctor complied with the request once he understood the situation, although he noted that today's general medical training teaches doctors not to prolong life in seriously ill patients.

A Different Value System

WHILE DOCTORS ARE TAUGHT TO BE CULTURALLY sensitive, society at large often has very different values than those treasured by our community, and the medical establishment has shifted its focus from achieving longevity to providing patients with a high quality of life. The vast majority of the world sees no reason to extend the life of someone who might be left with significant limitations; in one extreme case, I heard of a doctor telling a man that there was no point in taking heroic measures for his gravely ill wife since, if she survived, she would never be able to go to the mall. The concept that every day, week, month and year of life is precious is a foreign idea to many in the medical world, but taking the time to speak with

---

Rabbi Naftali Katz is a talmid of Beth Medrash Govoha and presently answers shailos for Chayim Aruchim, a division of Agudath Israel of America whose goal is to help the Jewish community make healthcare decisions according to halachah.

healthcare professionals and explain our beliefs can often open up a window to treatment that is consistent with our value system.

When encountering difficulties in patient care, it is important to understand that doctors are usually willing to work with patients and their families. Far from being an "us-versus-them" situation, these instances are demonstrative of the fact that our Torah-based lives are centered on different values than those maintained by society at large. It is important to stand our ground, albeit respectfully and with sensitivity, and to be in contact with a qualified *rav* who can be consulted when difficult situations arise.

AS IN SO MANY ASPECTS OF LIFE, IT IS CRUCIAL TO BE AN educated consumer when dealing with medical issues. Consider

Advocating for Your Loved One
getting a second opinion when offered a diagnosis and be sure to find out if there are other possible avenues of treatment that might be explored. In today's evolving medical world, it is important to understand the potential pitfalls and to realize which circumstances require careful monitoring and intervention in order to ensure the best possible outcome.

Nutrition is a critical element in patient care and one that is sometimes not adequately provided to terminally ill patients and the elderly. Lack of proper nutrition is often an issue with dementia patients and the forerunner of a host of other problems, such as infection, etc.; once a downward spiral begins, it can be extremely difficult to reverse. Furthermore, many in the medical world believe that an inability to drink is part of the dying process, often prompting them to withhold IV hydration from patients who can no longer hydrate themselves, a potentially disastrous decision. Given those realities, it is imperative to consult with a *rav*, alongside a doctor, as quickly as possible to discuss nutritional options, including artificial feeding via a PEG tube or other means, as well as hydration.

THE ACT OF SIGNING A **DO NOT** RESUSCITATE (DNR) ORDER has become alarmingly hazardous in recent years; with hospitals

Understanding Potential Dangers
routinely and persistently asking patients to sign a DNR upon admission, the consequences can be deadly. At Brigham

and Women's Hospital in Boston, researchers found that "mortality was over two times greater" for patients with DNRs than those without them. While those in our community who sign a DNR do so to prevent heroic measures from being taken in the event of a cardiac arrest or heart attack, many of today's medical staff view the declaration as a license to forego aggressive treatment in multiple situations. This has been corroborated in the Journal of Patient Safety. Do Not Intubate (DNI) orders have brought about similar issues. Therefore, a competent *rav* who is familiar with medical matters should be consulted in all situations to determine when and if either order should be signed.

Finally, while hospice care can offer certain benefits, it can also present its own set of challenges. Typically, hospices are designed to keep patients comfortable in end-of-life situations without much consideration given to prolonging life for as long as possible. While some hospice companies are open to accommodating requests from patients' families, it is important to remain vigilant to ensure that those providing the actual care will follow through with those orders as intended. Requests to provide hydration, antibiotics or other medications, or to draw blood to check for infections may run counter to the hospice model, making it crucial to keep a watchful eye on the patient at all times to ensure that he or she is receiving the desired level of care.

IN CLOSING, RAV GERSHON BESS, *SHLITA,* SHARED WITH me a story of a question that was brought to the Steipler Gaon

The Value of Every Minute of Life

about a particular *gadol* who was in a vegetative state toward the end of his life. The questioner wondered about the value of this great *rosh yeshivah's* life now that he could no longer be productive. Answering in his inimitable fashion, the Steipler quoted the Gemara in *Kiddushin* (40a) that says that one who wants to do a mitzvah but is incapable of doing so because of circumstances beyond his control is considered to have actually done the mitzvah and is rewarded accordingly. This esteemed *rosh yeshivah*, said the Steipler, spent his days *davening*, learning, teaching Torah, providing *chizzuk* to those in need and living a life filled with *avodas* Hashem, and now that he was incapable of doing his holy work, every day that he was still alive was considered as if he was continuing to fulfill those very same *mitzvos*. We need to view our own seriously ill loved ones in the same way, realizing that they gain eternal reward every minute that they are with us; when we look at them with this mindset, it will be easier to provide them with adequate and vigilant care, despite the fact that to the secular world their current existence seems to be lacking purpose.

A senior oncologist once told me that family members who make healthcare decisions for a loved one based on their own whims and preferences often suffer years of guilt later on, wondering if they made the right choices. In our world, however, the situation is vastly different, with Torah guidelines steering us in the proper direction, giving family members the security of knowing that every step taken during those difficult moments was done in accordance with *halachah*. Just as we live our lives based on the Torah's laws regarding Shabbos and kashrus observance although the outside world functions differently, we must also proceed according to Torah guidance regarding end-of-life medical decisions.

May we all be blessed with *siyata d'Shmaya* to care for our loved ones *al pi halachah*.

KEY POINTS:

- Society at large has changed from focusing on longevity to focusing on "quality of life."

- Most doctors are trained to be culturally sensitive and will often listen if one speaks respectfully about the patient's values and desire to continue living as an Orthodox Jew.

- It is important to educate oneself regarding medical issues and to explore various avenues of treatments, while understanding potential pitfalls one might encounter.

- Proper nutrition is a crucial element in caring for terminally ill or elderly patients. Lack of adequate nutrition can be a common problem with dementia patients and can lead to many other issues. Once a patient can no longer feed himself, a *rav* should be consulted about other options, such as inserting a feeding tube.

- It is also important to ensure that patients in medical facilities are being properly hydrated; many in the medical world believe that an inability to drink is simply part of the dying process.

- A competent *rav* should always be consulted before signing a DNR (Do Not Resuscitate) or DNI (Do Not Intubate) order, as the consequences of doing so can greatly affect the patients care.

- The goal at most hospices is to make the patients comfortable – not to prolong their lives. Even if the hospice agrees to the family's terms, one must keep vigilant watch over a loved one under their care.

- Seriously ill loved ones gain eternal reward during every minute they are in this world; it is crucial to provide them with adequate and vigilant care, although the secular world might fail to see the purpose in their existence.

Who Shall Live And Who Shall Die

DRAMATIC CHANGES IN THE DELIVERY OF MEDICAL
CARE TO CRITICALLY AND TERMINALLY ILL PATIENTS
THAT WILL ULTIMATELY AFFECT EVERYONE

Mr. Mark J. Kurzmann, ESQ.,
& Dr. Leon Zacharowicz, MD

A NEW COST-DRIVEN, POLITICALLY CORRECT APPROACH
to medical care now prevails in many of the leading medical centers

A Troubling New Approach to Medical Care

and hospitals worldwide. Its adherents exude dignity and confidence, but do not be deceived. They cannot be relied upon to see eye-to-eye with us in times of medical crisis.

It is now common for hospitals and doctors to try to avoid their legal obligations to deliver patient care that conforms to the law. They are very resourceful and express this in a variety of creative ways. Unfortunately, a large segment of the religious public is ill-equipped to cope with the recent changes in medical ethics and care.

Both of us – one a physician and the other an attorney – have confronted this phenomenon at close range and have some practical advice to share with you, since sooner or later virtually all of us will

---

Mr. Mark J. Kurzmann, Esq., is a former US Department of Justice national security and civil litigator now in private practice. He has advocated for patients across the country in end-of-life and related matters, and has spoken on the subject extensively. He is also one of the few American lawyers who attended the Edmond Sarfa murder trial in Monaco.

Dr. Leon Zacharowicz, MD, MA, a neurologist, is a cofounder, together with Rav Yaakov Weiner, of the international Yarchei Kallah seminars on medical halachah, which since 1998 have exposed hundreds of medical personnel and rabbanim to contemporary issues. He has also counseled and testified on behalf of families opposed to withdrawal of life support from their loved ones in the US, Canada, and Europe.

face the challenge of arranging medical care for someone suffering from a critical or terminal illness.

As Jews, we are obligated to respect every moment of human life as being of infinite and immeasurable value. To survive both the overt and subtle pressures to abandon this religious imperative requires thorough *halachic,* emotional, and legal preparation. It also often requires unshakable faith, iron determination, and titanic courage.

AN OUNCE OF LEGAL PREVENTION, IN THE FORM OF A properly executed **Halachic Advance Medical Directive or Halachic Health-Care Proxy**, can be worth a pound

Tools to Protect Yourself

of medical-legal cure. However, the legally valid form alone is not always enough. Protecting yourselves and your loved ones from the troubling changes under which medical care is delivered in the US and Canada requires insight into what is actually going on in practice.

The pressures and coercive atmosphere can be nearly unbearable. Consider the following two illustrations:

In a landmark Canadian case that attracted international attention a few years ago, Samuel Golubchuk, *z"l,* a hospitalized Orthodox Jewish patient who was conscious but unable to speak, was written off by his attending physicians. He was not terminal and was not at all near death.

The hospital staff in Winnipeg, however, was unwilling to keep this disabled elderly man alive despite the protests of his adult children. Treating him was an endeavor the professionals considered futile. Reportedly, one of his doctors actually referred to ongoing treatment as "torture." So, they concluded, the only ethical thing to do was to withdraw life support, which would quickly lead to his demise. Among other things, it took an affidavit by one of us (Zacharowicz), challenging the misleading representation of the patient's condition by the medical professionals, to prompt a judge to issue a series of court orders that sustained the patient's life. Ironically, these doctors were adhering to the professional standards of the regional medical society, which *required* the treating physician to terminate the life of a patient whose quality of life, in the sole judgment of that physician, fell below a certain level.

The experience of another patient illustrates how the pressure applied by the very people upon whom we rely to treat our loved ones is devoid of our notions of ethics and basic fairness. An elderly concentration-camp survivor who had experienced horrific health-related ordeals in the camps had for years delegated all significant medical decisions to someone else, unwilling to face the emotional stress of making such decisions alone. Despite being otherwise lucid, he simply lacked the capacity to again confront the very thin line separating life from death.

Upon admission less than a year ago to one of the world's leading hospitals, a standard New York State Department of Health health-care proxy form was handed to him for signature. The hospital administration was particularly unhappy because the patient had the audacity to fill in several blank spaces and document his express wish to be kept alive despite advanced age and tenuous health.

This elderly person was suffering from a serious disease, but most assuredly was not dying. He was neither vegetative nor comatose. He could communicate and converse. Yet he would not (and could not) make healthcare decisions without assistance. The health-care proxy form directed the physicians and nurses to follow the instructions of his designated health-care agent, with the objective of quality care, treatment, and maintenance of life.

The hospital refused to do so. It elected to ignore the health-care proxy on the legal grounds that it was not yet operative under New York law because the patient was otherwise lucid and communicative. No exceptions.

When challenged, the hospital professionals ignored the patient's inability to make medical decisions which, in the legal opinion of one of us (Kurzmann) who was advising the health-care agent, empowered that agent to make any and all health decisions. The individual's health-care agent then demanded a review by the hospital's ethics committee.

Before the full committee convened, two of its members, who realized that the hospital's position was weak, decided to take matters into their own hands. They sequestered the patient in a private room, closed the door, and barred access by the designated health-care agent. They then persuaded the patient to sign the standard New York form in blank as part of their scheme to implement the hospital's agenda.

This, they reasoned, would deprive the healthcare agent of any legally enforceable objection to the patient's demise by their preferred method of death: one with "dignity." It was only after this ruse was exposed that the ethics committee was constrained to back down.

These two incidents are not exaggerated or isolated events. They reflect a trend that is prevalent and growing rapidly. Yet as Jews, we have a solemn obligation to safeguard the gift of human life and never actively shorten a person's life. This applies no matter how painful, seemingly unconscious, or excruciatingly sad each second of life might appear to us as observers.

Sadly, our views no longer seem to matter to many policymakers. The once sacred notion of patient autonomy has been usurped by doctors who apparently feel that they alone should determine who shall live and who shall die.

Lest you believe that this phenomenon is restricted to our community, think again. Only last month there was vigorous national debate over whether former Vice President Dick Cheney, who is only seventy-one years of age, was deserving of a heart transplant.

Although he benefitted from no preferential treatment and had to wait twenty months for a donor organ, many expressed the belief that a younger person should have received it instead – a position antithetical to *halachah*.

This is but the tip of the iceberg. Routinely, families of patients deemed by the healthcare industry to be too expensive to treat or otherwise unworthy of life-sustaining treatment are urged to choose a less costly alternative.

AS A GENERAL RULE OF THUMB, IT IS ABSOLUTELY essential that every adult sign and have proper witnesses to a **Tools to Protect Yourself** *halachically-approved* medical directive or health-care proxy and submit it to the US Living Will Registry. These simple forms and clear instructions are readily available at no cost from the Agudath Israel of America and the Orthodox Union. No lawyer or notary public is required, although you may wish to consult your *rav* or attorney. It is equally important to have a copy to present to the admissions staff if and when you or your loved one is treated at a healthcare facility. If a patient has not signed a *halachically-approved* form before admission, then someone must consult the family *rav* or *posek* immediately before the patient signs anything. Under virtually no circumstances should anyone sign in blank the standard health-care proxy form, **Do Not Resuscitate** (DNR), **Do Not Intubate** (DNI), or a similar form handed routinely to patients upon admission, without first having a thorough *halachic* consultation, which should preferably involve a physician knowledgeable about the patient's disease and sympathetic to our community's values and beliefs.

Although the practical implementation of these legal instruments can at times be a challenge in and of itself, not taking the few minutes needed to complete and submit a health-care advance directive or proxy may prove to be a fatal mistake. Further, it is absolutely essential that family members discreetly monitor a patient's condition and care constantly and with great vigilance and in close consultation with a sympathetic physician and *rav*.

We ask each and every person to take a few minutes to sign the necessary documents that may spell the difference between life and death for you and your loved ones.

Reprinted with permission from Ami Magazine.

KEY POINTS:

- Due to the recent increased focus on a cost-driven, politically correct approach to medical care, we cannot rely on hospitals and physicians to be on the same page as us in times of medical crisis.

- As Jews, we are obligated to respect every moment of human life as precious.

- Understanding the current attitude toward medical care in the United States and Canada is essential to protecting yourself and your family when in need of medical care.

- Patient autonomy is increasingly being overruled by doctors who feel that they should decide who should live and who should die.

- Routinely, families of patients deemed "too expensive" to treat or unworthy of treatment for some other reason are urged to choose less costly alternatives.

- It is essential for every adult to sign a *halachically* approved medical directive and/or healthcare proxy, with proper witnesses, and to submit these documents to the US Living Will Registry. Both documents are available online from Agudath Israel and the Orthodox Union.

- It is important to present a copy of the abovementioned documents to the administrative staff at any facility providing care to you or a loved one.

- Never sign a blank, standard healthcare proxy, DNR (**D**o **N**ot **R**esuscitate) or DNI (**D**o **N**ot **I**ntubate) that is routinely handed to patients upon admission. Always speak to a knowledgeable *rav* first.

- It is essential for family members to discreetly monitor their loved one's condition and care in any facility and to consult regularly with a sympathetic physician and knowledgeable *rav*.

A Ticket to Olam Haba

THE VALUE OF SAYING VIDUY

Rabbi Elchonon Zohn

כל המתודה יש לו חלק בעולם הבא

All those who say *viduy* have a portion in the World to Come
(*Shulchan Aruch, Yoreh Dei'ah 338:1*).

BASED ON A MISHNAH *(SANHEDRIN 6:2),* THE *Shulchan Aruch* attests that anyone who says *viduy* (the deathbed confession) receives *Olam Haba* – an infinite reward. Imagine the kindness inherent in that promise. The Mishnah learns this from Achan, whose story is recounted in *Sefer Yehoshua* (*Yehoshua, 7*). In the *zechus* (merit) of his saying *viduy*, he earned *Olam Haba,* even though his sin was so severe that he had been condemned to death. The Shelah HaKaddosh writes that inspiring a *choleh* (sick person) to say *viduy* is an integral aspect of *bikur cholim* (visiting the sick). If helping to ease the physical pain and aid the physical well-being of one who is ill is a great mitzvah, how much greater a mitzvah is it to inspire them and assure the eternal well-being of their *neshamah*, their soul! Underscoring that concept is the *tzava'ah* (ethical will) of Rabi Eliezer HaGadol, which states, "One who oversees the welfare of a *choleh* and makes an effort to ascertain that he does *teshuvah* (repents), his reward is very great…"

We are all familiar with the *viduy* we say in *selichos* and in the Yom Kippur *davening* (prayer service). At the conclusion of Yom Kippur, we are cleansed and purified and have likely taken on new *kabbalos*

Rabbi Elchonon Zohn founded the National Association of Chevra Kadisha (NASCK) as a unifying entity for Chevros Kadisha throughout the United States and Canada. He has been the Director of the Chevrah Kadisha of the Va'ad Harabbanim of Queens for over thirty years. Rabbi Zohn received semichah from Yeshivas Chofetz Chaim.

(spiritual resolutions) to help us remain so. But a short while later, many of us revert to our old habits and return to our old routines. The *viduy* we say just before our passing is quite different. The atonement of the deathbed *viduy* is long-lasting. Despite this extraordinary *zechus,* the *Shulchan Aruch* – in the very same paragraph in which it mentions the reward for saying *viduy* – warns that suggesting to a deathly ill person that the time has come to say *viduy* might frighten them to the extent that it actually hastens their demise. So practically, how do we balance these two powerful, yet competing concerns?

What is *viduy*, and why is it so important?

Viduy, confessing one's transgressions, is one of the *taryag* (613) *mitzvos* (*Sefer Hamitzvos, positive commandment 73*). It is the part of doing *teshuvah* that involves verbally articulating one's sins. The traditional prayer of *viduy* is repeated throughout the Yom Kippur prayers because it is part of how we achieve atonement on that holy day.

It is understandable that in the last moments of life, a person would want to do *teshuvah* in order to return to their Creator with a clean slate. Those familiar with the concept of *teshuvah* will note that the literal definition of the word *teshuvah* is "return." This is the first word in the *haftorah* we read during the *Aseres Yemei Teshuvah* (Ten Days of Repentance), on Shabbos Shuvah: "Return, Yisrael, to Hashem, Your G-d, for you have stumbled by your sins" (*Hoshea 14:2*). "Doing *teshuvah*" implies returning to Hashem's ways with a cleansed *neshamah*. How very fitting is it, then, that when dying – when actually returning one's soul to Hashem – a person would want and need to be engaged in the act of *teshuvah*. The specific *viduy* at the end of life includes an acceptance of one's imminent death and embraces one's passing as a means of *kapparah* – atonement. (See the text of *viduy* later in this article.)

How can one suggest *viduy* to a *choleh mesukan* (critically ill person) without causing great distress?

The *Shulchan Aruch* (*Y.D. 338:1*) itself gives guidance on how to approach this delicate matter.

It advises that when suggesting the recital of *viduy*, the sick person should be told three things: The first is that saying *viduy* does not, *chas v'Shalom* (G-d forbid), indicate acceptance of their imminent death. Rather, the *Shulchan Aruch* instructs, "Say to them, 'Many have said *viduy* and did not die.'"

Once relaxed somewhat about the prospect of saying *viduy*, the *choleh* should be reminded that if they do not say it now, there is a real possibility that they might lose the opportunity to say it: "And many have died without saying *viduy*."

Finally, they should be reminded that saying *viduy*, an act of *teshuvah*, can actually give them the merit of continued life: "As a reward for saying *viduy*, you should continue to live."

We finish by wishing them a *refuah shleimah* (complete recovery) (*Gesher HaChayim 1:4:1*).

In short, when bringing up the idea of *viduy*, we should emphasize to the sick person that there is nothing to be lost by saying *viduy*; on the contrary, there is everything to be gained, both in the Next World, and very possibly, even in this one.

The *Gesher HaChayim* (*1:5:3*) elaborates on this concern by citing "a great and noteworthy procedure established at Bikur Cholim Hospital in Yerushalayim, in which a G-d fearing individual would stand in the hallway of the hospital each morning and would recite the *viduy* out loud, and all the patients would recite it along with him. Knowing this to be the daily custom, the *cholim* would recite the *viduy* with confidence and an uplifted spirit." The *Gesher HaChayim* also references the *Chochmas Adam* (*151:11*), who cites a similar *minhag* (custom) observed in many European cities and specifically in Berlin.

How does one say *viduy*?

The recitation of *viduy* can be extremely emotional, for both the sick person and their loved ones. For that reason, the best procedure is to have everyone exit the room, leaving only the person saying *viduy* and the person who will help them say it (*Shulchan Aruch Y.D. 338:1*).

It is important, however, to inform family that *viduy* was said. It will give them comfort knowing it was taken care of, and they will know that *they* do not need to raise the issue. Letting the family know that their loved one has said *viduy* is also likely to sensitize them to the frame of mind of the *choleh*.

When dealing with a nonobservant family, it is important that the family be informed before discussing *viduy* with the *choleh*. Explain the concept to them; if they are accepting of it, they will likely be an asset when suggesting to the *choleh* to say *viduy*. (We will elaborate on how to broach *viduy* with a nonobservant *choleh* later in this article.) If, on the other hand, they are not comfortable with the idea, at least they will not be angry to hear if it had been done without their knowledge. It has been my experience that when the concept of *viduy* is explained, the vast majority of nonobservant Jews appreciate and embrace it.

The sick person then gives *tzedakah*. This charity should be specifically designated for the poor, rather than given to an organization supporting other causes, however worthy (*Gesher HaChayim 1:5:7, as cited in The Mourner's Companion*).

The actual text of *viduy* to be recited will vary depending on the physical capability and level of knowledge of the person saying it. Someone stronger can say a longer *viduy;* someone weaker will likely have to say a shorter *viduy*. While it is beneficial to have the *choleh*'s fullest degree of concentration and understanding, it is important not to tax their strength (*Gesher HaChayim 1:5*). In addition, a person less familiar with *viduy* might find the more complete version cumbersome and perhaps overwhelming and confusing.

Viduy is also a most appropriate time for the *choleh* to forgive anyone who ever wronged them and to ask forgiveness of anyone they ever wronged (*Chochmas Adam 151:12*); the person saying *viduy* should be instructed to do both of these things. While it is obviously best in the latter case to ask forgiveness directly from the person they have wronged, if this is impossible (as it usually is in the case of a deathbed *viduy*), it is sufficient for the sick person to pray to be forgiven by others and to articulate that request. This is similar to what is said in *Tefillah Zakkah* before *Kol Nidrei*.

When is it too soon to say *viduy*?

Just as it is never "too soon" to do *teshuvah*, it is never "too soon" to say *viduy*. One way of reducing anxiety around saying *viduy* is to say it whenever confronting a medical event that has potential danger, such as surgery.

A prominent member of our women's *chevrah kaddisha* would ask me to say *viduy* with her before she underwent any procedure that required general anesthesia. I said *viduy* with her at least three or four times, the last time just a few hours before her *petirah* (passing)*,* when she could no longer speak but was still aware of what I was saying and could think along with my words. A friend of mine shared with me that his father recited *viduy* five or six times before his actual passing; not only did he say *viduy* before each surgery, he also said it when he was transferred to the critical care unit.

My mother, *a"h*, who passed away over 25 years ago, always said she wanted to die in her sleep, as she was afraid of lengthy suffering and even more so of burdening those around her. I would tell her that Ya'akov Avinu asked to be ill so he could prepare for his death and that being sick had important advantages. At the end of her life, living in Yerushalayim, she was admitted to the hospital for a suspected heart attack. However, she experienced no pain and seemed well. That evening, many grandchildren and other family members gathered in her room, and she captivated them with stories from her childhood in Lithuania.

The next morning, my sister came to see her and consult with her doctors. As she stood outside our mother's room, a doctor emerged, shaken. He said that as he was examining her, she suddenly died. He believed she had had an aortic rupture, which leads to instant death. *Retzon yerei'av ya'aseh* – her wish had been fulfilled.

When getting up from *shivah*, my sister remarked to our father, *zt"l*, that our mother often had "premonitions" about important events that were soon to occur. She was surprised that our mother had not had a feeling that she was on the verge of the most important event in her life – her own impending passing – and that, consequently, she was not able to say *viduy*. He replied that, in fact, she did have such a feeling. After everyone had left her room the night before she passed away, she had called him and asked him to come to the hospital. When he got there, she told him that although she was feeling well, she felt it would be a good idea to say *viduy*, especially since the doctors were concerned about her heart. And so he said *viduy* with her.

It gave all of us great comfort to know that our mother, *a"h*, who grew up in the Mir, was from a family of Litvishe *roshei yeshivah* (heads of Lithuanian yeshivahs) and who fully understood the value of *viduy* did not forfeit that *zechus* by having her wish for a *misas neshikah* (peaceful death) fulfilled and that she had merited to say the full *viduy* before her passing.

When is it too late to say *viduy?*

As long as a person is alive, it is not too late for them to say *viduy*. *The tefillah can and should be said with someone who can no longer speak.* Someone can say *viduy* in the *choleh*'s presence and ask them to think along with the words being said. Doing so allows the person to fulfill the mitzvah and gain the merit. (This works through the concept of *shomei'a k'oneh*: one who hears is considered as one who responds.) When saying *viduy* in this situation, it should be said in the first person, using the word "I," so that the person can think along with the words being spoken.

What if someone is unconscious?

Not only can one say *viduy* with someone who can no longer speak, a person who is in a coma or is unconscious for any other reason can also be led in *viduy*. One should tell them to think along with the words being spoken and should not assume that this effort is in any way pointless.

People who have woken from comas commonly say that they were aware of events around them, including everything that was said. (This also teaches a valuable lesson about how very careful one must be regarding what they say in the presence of someone in a coma, but that is beyond the scope of this article.)

I remember saying *viduy* with a congregant of mine who had had a stroke and was considered to be brain dead. This man, whom I'll call Reb Yudel, was in his early 80s. He had escaped to the United States before the Holocaust. He was not a learned man, but someone I would call very "traditional."

One day, while I was visiting him, he went into cardiac arrest. This was in the days before DNR (Do Not Resuscitate) orders were routinely given for such patients. I was rushed out of the room, and a horde of medical personnel succeeded in stabilizing him. I was a young rabbi at that time, and I suddenly realized that Reb Yudel might not be with us much longer. I understood that I should say *viduy* with him sooner than later.

I went home, took my rabbi's *madrich* (manual) and went back to the hospital. When I returned to his room, I sat on his bed, took his hand, broached the subject of *viduy* in the way the *Shulchan Aruch* instructs and told him in Yiddish, "Reb Yudel, I'm going to say *viduy* with you."

Although he had been declared brain dead and despite the fact that he had just been resuscitated after a "code," he gripped my hand very, very tightly. I knew that Reb Yudel had been a butcher and marveled at the strength of his grasp. I said the introduction in Yiddish and the *viduy* in both Hebrew and Yiddish. He clenched my hand the entire time.

When I finished saying *viduy*, he released my hand. Although Reb Yudel was not learned and was not even a fully practicing Jew, it was clear to me that he understood not only what I was saying to him, but also the significance of it. I was sure it was ingrained in his mind from his childhood in Europe.

What is the text of *viduy*?

The *nusach* used for *viduy* is dependent on the strength of the person who is ill. If they would like to – and are physically capable of it – the *choleh* should say the entire *viduy* of Yom Kippur. There are also several chapters of Tehillim, as well as other *tefillos*, that can be said at that time. Many *siddurim* and other *sefarim* contain the *viduy, and some list other things to be said, as well as minhagim for the moment of petirah.*

The basic *viduy* prayer, as written in the *Shulchan Aruch* (*Y.D. 338:2*) is:

מוֹדֶה אֲנִי לְפָנֶיךָ ה' אֱ-לֹקַי וֵא-לֹקֵי אֲבוֹתַי, שֶׁרְפוּאָתִי וּמִיתָתִי בְּיָדֶךָ. יְהִי רָצוֹן מִלְפָנֶיךָ שֶׁתִּרְפָּאֵנִי רְפוּאָה שְׁלֵמָה. וְאִם אָמוּת תְּהֵא מִיתָתִי כַּפָּרָה עַל כָּל הַחֲטָאִים וְעֲוֹנוֹת וְהַפְּשָׁעִים שֶׁחָטָאתִי וְשֶׁעָוִיתִי וְשֶׁפָּשַׁעְתִּי לְפָנֶיךָ וְתֵן חֶלְקִי בְּגַן עֵדֶן, וְזַכֵּנִי לְעוֹלָם הַבָּא הַצָּפוּן לַצַּדִּיקִים.

I acknowledge before You, Hashem, my G-d and G-d of my fathers, that my recovery and my death are in Your hands. May it be Your will to heal me completely. And if I die, may my passing be an atonement for all the sins that I have committed and grant me my portion in Gan Eden and allow me to merit the World to Come, which has been reserved for the righteous.

If a person is too weak to say this entire paragraph, they can fulfill the mitzvah by stating simply:

יְהִי רָצוֹן שֶׁתְּהֵא מִיתָתִי כַּפָּרָה עַל כָּל עֲוֹנוֹתָי.

May it be Your will that my death be an atonement for all my sins.
(Based on the *Rema* on *Shulchan Aruch Y.D. 338:1*.)

The text brought in *Gesher HaChayim* (*1:5:5*), quoted by Chevrah Lomdei Mishnah in the *Final Prayers* pamphlet, is as follows:

אִם חַס וְשָׁלוֹם אָמוּת, תְּהֵא מִיתָתִי כַּפָּרָה עַל כָּל עֲוֹנוֹתַי.

If, G-d forbid I die, may my death be an atonement for all my sins.

How can one approach the topic of *viduy* with someone who is not observant?

Although Reb Yudel was not fully observant as an adult, he had been raised in a religious family. It is understandably more difficult to broach the topic of *viduy* with someone who is completely unfamiliar with it, who may not have a definite belief in Hashem, who may, *chas v'Shalom*, be angry at his lot in life, or who may even think of *viduy* as a non-Jewish rite.

I have had significant success with such people using the following technique: I begin by focusing on the thought that serious illness is a time for serious thinking. I might spend time discussing belief in an afterlife; the eternity of the soul; belief in Hashem, the Creator; the Jewish view of reward and punishment; the power of prayer; and other such topics. I also mention that although we are always hopeful and pray that we will prevail over our illness and live much longer, we know that no one lives forever.

I then suggest that whenever the time arrives to meet our Creator, wouldn't we want to be on the best terms possible? We may have gone through life questioning some of His decisions. We may have even felt resentment or anger about the hand we were dealt in life. However, we must honestly acknowledge that He likely questioned some of our choices and decisions, as well. Isn't *this* an appropriate time to make up? Why not consider utilizing this serious moment to forgive Him – and perhaps others as well – and ask Him to forgive us?

When the person is in this frame of mind and accepts this point, it is quite natural to invite them to say the most essential words of *viduy* (using the basic *viduy* prayer, or the simpler, one-line version). These words represent acceptance of the possibility of their death, regret for their misdeeds in life, and the request that if they do pass away, their passing should grant them atonement.

Too many people are uncomfortable about raising the issue of *viduy* and then find that it has become too late to do so. It is unfortunate that either because of their preoccupation with the myriad challenges that illness presents, or out of fear of broaching the subject, many people allow a loved one to pass away without ever saying *viduy*.

We are all aware of the great kindness it is to ease the burden of a sick person and to help them recover physically. How much more kind is it to create a path for their *spiritual* recovery and put them on the road to *Olam Haba?* We need to overcome our discomfort and fear, say *viduy* ourselves when appropriate, and encourage others to do so, as well. The *zechus* for both is eternal and infinite.

KEY POINTS:

- One who recites *viduy* is assured that he will merit *Olam Haba*.

- Inspiring an ill person to say *viduy* is part of the mitzvah of *bikur cholim*.

- The recitation of *viduy* – the confession of one's sins – is one of the 613 *mitzvos*.

- It is imperative to balance inspiring the ill person to say *viduy* with not frightening them and *chas v'shalom* hastening their death by doing so.

- The *Shulchan Aruch* offers specific guidelines for how to carefully approach an ill person regarding the recitation of *viduy*. The goal is to convey that in reciting *viduy* there is nothing to be lost and everything to be gained – both in this world and the next: many have said *viduy* and lived; many have died without having said *viduy*; reciting *viduy* should be a merit for the ill person to live.

- The best practice for reciting *viduy* with an ill person is to have only one person remain in the room to help the ill person in doing so.

- Be sure to inform family members that *viduy* was said.

- When the family is not observant, it is important to apprise them before discussing *viduy* with the ill person.

- After reciting *viduy*, the ill person should give *tzedakah*, specifically for poor people.

- The length of the text recited can vary, depending on the ability and condition of the ill person.

- The time of *viduy* recitation is also an appropriate chance for the ill person to forgive others and to ask forgiveness of those whom he has wronged.

- It is **never too soon** to recite *viduy*. It is a good practice to recite *viduy* before any medical procedure that is potentially dangerous.

- It is **never too late** to recite *viduy*. It can be said with someone who can no longer speak. The ill person can be asked to think along with the words as they are recited. This can even be done with someone who is unconscious or unresponsive.

- It can be difficult to broach the subject of *viduy* with one who is not observant. One can do so by delicately suggesting that illness is a time for serious introspection and opening a discussion about the afterlife, the soul and G-d and that while we hope the ill person will recover, no one lives forever. Why not take the opportunity to be on the best terms possible with our Creator?

- It is a great kindness to ease the physical plight of a sick person; how much more important it is to assist in their spiritual recovery by ensuring the recitation of *viduy*.

Following is a reproducible copy of the EMES (Emergency Medical Education and Sign-Up) card, which was created with the guidance of Agudath Israel's legal staff and should be completed by every person over the age of 18. It should be kept with your license or ID card, clearly displaying your end-of-life wishes in case of an emergency. For more information, please contact NASCK at (718) 847-6280 or (888) 243-8721, or email info@nasck.org.

Emergency Medical Instructions

Agent: (print)_____

Office:_____ Home: _____

Cell:_____

Email:_____

Alternate Agent: (print) _____

Office:_____ Home: _____

Cell:_____

Email:_____

Rabbi: (print)_____

Office:_____ Home: _____

Cell:_____

Email:_____

EMERGENCY MEDICAL AND POST-MORTEM INSTRUCTIONS

I (print name)_____ have executed a

- □ Agudath Israel of America "Halachic Medical Directive"
- □ Rabbinical Council of America "Halachic Health Care Proxy"
- □ Health Care Proxy / Living Will
- □ US Living Will Registry® Reg.#_____
- □ None of the above.

Based on my religious and moral beliefs, I hereby direct that pending contact with my agent and/or Rabbi (designated below), health care providers immediately undertake all life-sustaining and emergency measures on my behalf. I further direct that in the event of my death, my agent shall be responsible for the disposition of my remains. I object to and direct that no autopsy, dissection or other post-mortem procedures, including organ donation, be performed on my body (unless I have directed otherwise in a written instrument). I also object to cremation of my body.

Signature: _____

Executed in: (County, State) _____ Date: _____

DECLARATION OF WITNESSES

We the undersigned declare, under penalty of perjury, that the person who has issued these "Emergency Instructions" is personally known to each of us and signed this document in our presence while appearing to be of sound mind and acting willingly and free from duress. Neither of us is appointed as an agent by this document.

Witnesses:

Witness 1: (sign) _____ Date:_____

Name of Witness 1: (print) _____

Residing at: _____

Witness 2: (sign) _____ Date:_____

Name of Witness 2: (print) _____

Residing at: _____

CONCISE LAWS OF SHIVAH:

This pamphlet can alleviate much uncertainty and stress, offering clear, concise and definitive *halachic pesak* for the *aninus* and *shivah* periods. The Hebrew text and English translation have both been reviewed and approved by Rav Yaakov Forchheimer, senior *posek* in Beth Medrash Govoha, Lakewood, NJ.

THE NESHAMAH SHOULD HAVE AN ALIYAH:

A unique volume explaining the concept of providing merit for a soul and offering practical guidance for *aliyas neshamah* opportunities.

I LOST SOMEONE SPECIAL:

A picture book introducing young children to the concept of remaining linked to one who has passed away by earning *zechusim* on their behalf.

NICHUM V'NECHAMAH:
TO COMFORT AND BE COMFORTED

An invaluable guide to the mitzvah of *nichum aveilim*, offering guidance and comfort to mourners and comforters. Includes special Woman to Woman subsection.
– Available in three separate formats: book, DVD, or MP3.

THE YAHRTZEIT COMPANION:

A comprehensive, compact guide to make the most of this significant day. Includes appropriate prayers, mishnayos, translation, and practical guidelines.

COMFORT, COURAGE & CLARITY:

Finding Inner Peace through the Challenge of Loss.
An innovative book that provides guidance and support for those who have lost a parent. Includes material that can be used in a support-group setting, an explanation of the grieving process, helpful quotes and a "feelings guide."

Services

SIYUM MISHNAYOS

Celebrate a *siyum mishnayos* to mark a *shloshim, yahrtzeit,* or both. Chevrah Lomdei Mishnah's accomplished *talmidei chachamim* can complete any *masechta* or *seder* or even the entire *Shishah Sidrei Mishnah* to help you accomplish this goal.

SIYUM GEMARA

Celebrate a *siyum Gemara to* secure an even greater *zechus* for a loved one's *shloshim* or *yahrtzeit.* Chevrah Lomdei Mishnah's *talmidei chachamim* can complete any *masechta* or *seder* or even the entire *Shas Bavli.*

DAILY MISHNAH/GEMARA STUDY

A *talmid chacham* will learn a portion of Mishnah or Gemara each day, for a year, in memory of your loved one.

KADDISH RECITAL

One of our *talmidei chachamim* is available to recite Kaddish for the first eleven months after passing. Also available for any *yahrtzeit.*

SPECIFIC MISHNAH STUDY FOR *SHLOSHIM/YAHRTZEIT*

An accomplished *talmid chacham* can study the *perakim* of Mishnah traditionally learned on a *shloshim* and/or *yahrtzeit.* These include the 7th *perek* of Mikvaos, the 24th *perek* of Keilim, the *perakim* beginning with the letters of the name of the *niftar,* and Masechta Chagigah.

For more information about Chevrah Lomdei Mishnah's programs and services, contact us at **(732) 364-7029** or **info@ChevrahLomdeiMishnah.org** or visit **www.ChevrahLomdeiMishnah.org**

PROVIDE
ETERNAL MERIT
FOR YOUR
DEPARTED
LOVED ONE

**KADDISH RECITAL, MISHNAH AND GEMARA STUDY
OPPORTUNITIES AVAILABLE**

---

(732) 364-7029
info@ChevrahLomdeiMishnah.org
www.ChevrahLomdeiMishnah.org